the
lonely
crowd

the lonely crowd
new home of the short story

Edited & Designed by John Lavin
Advisory Editor Michou Burckett St. Laurent
Contributing Editor Dan Coxon
Front & Back Cover Photos by Jo Mazelis
Frontispiece from 'The Dancers' by Constantinos Andronis

Published by The Lonely Press, 2017
Printed in Wales by Gwasg Gomer
Copyright The Lonely Crowd & its contributors, 2017

ISBN 978-0-9932368-5-3

*The Lonely Crowd is an entirely self-funded enterprise. Please
consider supporting us by subscribing to the magazine here*
www.thelonelycrowd.org/the-lonely-store
If you would like to advertise in The Lonely Crowd please email
ads@thelonelycrowd.org

Please direct all other enquiries to
johnlavin@thelonelycrowd.org
*Visit our website for more new short fiction, poetry, critical
writing & photography* www.thelonelycrowd.org

Contents

Smoke Alys Conran - **9**

Three Poems Nia Davies - **14**

Girlgrief Nuala O'Connor - **20**

Persephone Robert Minhinnick - **23**

Three Poems Mari Ellis Dunning - **34**

Feathering the Blade Emily Devane - **40**

Fango in the Mire Derwen Morfayel - **50**

Three Poems Niall Griffiths - **59**

Letters Above the Door Neil Campbell - **64**

Houtsiplou Kate North - **73**

The Two Parties Gary Raymond - **87**

You're all Playing It Wrong Anne Griffin - **96**

Joe Jeanette Sheppard - **105**

Three Poems Rhian Elizabeth - **113**

That Face, Like a Harvest Moon Susmita Bhattacharya - **117**

Smile Harder Richard Smyth - **127**

The Dancers Constantinos Andronis - **137**

Three Poems Ingrid Casey - **150**

Colours Nora Shychuk - **153**

Cat in a Bag Tony Bianchi - **164**

Dazzle Iain Robinson - **175**

Three Poems Lane Ashfeldt - **182**

Bánh ga to John Saul - **187**

On the Mattress Lander Hawes - **200**

Three Poems Ellen Davies - **211**
And Three Things Bumped Kelly Creighton - **214**
The Package Mark Blayney - **233**
Two Poems Jackie Gorman - **247**
Flood Paul Davenport-Randell - **249**
Lucca: Last Days of a Marriage Tom Vowler - **261**
Three Poems Sue Moules - **274**
Magnolias Bethany W. Pope - **277**
Lledrith Diana Powell - **285**
Three Poems Kathy Miles - **303**
Sometimes There's God Jon Boilard - **307**

About the Authors - **350**

issue six

Smoke
Alys Conran

It started with the things furthest away. It wasn't so much that you saw the buildings, the pylons, the trees, slouching on the horizon, like flags after a breeze, as that you felt them. You felt them, lying down, giving up. A sort of sagging far away, coming closer. It arrived at the end of the street, arrived with a sigh, the faint but tremendous feeling of exhalation, of something let down. There was no point then, as you stood in your kitchen at the kettle, holding it, thinking of lifting it for the tea. There was no point in any more of these actions. It was ungathering toward you, unpiling the shelves, letting the doors creak ajar, making gaps around the windows and sagging at the slate roof. On the kettle, your hand was limp, loosening from the handle.

She comes at three, the girl with the bright cheeks, with the tea, poured from a big metal canister, a button on the side to make the hot water come. She sets the cup on your table, the table with legs that are wheeled around your chair so you don't spill.

She's solid, saying 'Nice cup of tea, Edward. Nice cup of tea.' And it is, when she holds it to your lips. Hot water, tea, milk. A nice cup of tea. 'Sugar, Edward?'

She knows the answer. It's to get you to speak. You speak.

'No,' you say, your voice almost transparent.

9

'Sweet enough already!' she says with her clear, all there voice.

In the next bed to yours someone's going on and on about D-Day.

'Did you fight in the war?' she asks you, her question pulling it all together again.

It didn't matter how dark it was in the city, how many windows they covered right to the corners, how many streetlamps were left unlit. They still fell. At night the city was a black iris, turned up, watching the sky. You worked nights. It was six nights, and then a night off. The nights of rest were the worst.

Then you'd to stay in the black house, shut up like a closed lid. Blind to it. And one of them might fall on you, and you'd perhaps not wake. Like that body you found, in the boy's house, melted into her bed. When you think of it your body comes apart along the seam of your spine, like a split city.

The bomb you saw fall was black and long. It fell from the sky, and you saw it hit, two streets away. When it hits there's a couple of seconds of memory unaccounted for. Things are separate, body from sound and sight, until they come back together again, and you start running toward the place it's left, the building just a bitten hole, and the flames lusty and slurping.

It was *put the fire out, smother the fire and get them out* any way you could and to safety. Even if it was through a window. Climb the ladder, put up against the side of the smoking house, and lift the hot, miraculous child from the window ledge where he sits, eyes two lenses, waiting with nothing in his eyes. Set his feet onto the ladder and get him to climb down between you and the rungs, your body sheltering him, your body around his little beating heart.

That boy Isaac was one of the only ones you remember. He'd had his photograph taken afterwards for the paper. A survivor, the only one of the night. The boy was taken to Wales or Cumbria on a bus. They sent some of them to fresh air, away from the clattering sky. His face fades and breaks apart, away to Wales or Cumbria. On a bus.

She asks you, and you see his eyes. Black almost. Looking up at that house. His look charred dark by the fire.

The man next to you, in his white-sheeted, clean bed, is telling the girl about Normandy, how he crawled through the bushes, kept awake all night to keep alive, how he ate nothing for three days. He has flopped hands, and Benidorm freckled skin. His hands shape the places and things he makes in his mind as he speaks into her cleanness. You look at her, thinking what to say, your mind just black, gnashing sky.

'I don't remember,' you mouth, the words barely fizzing through your lungs.

You could reach out and touch her. You could reach out and touch her. But your hands are just a tracing, and your voice is barely a note. She wheels the clattering trolley out of your room and down the corridor. In the corridor the echoes and voices of this place swallow her slowly. You sit, listening, worrying faintly for her. Someone so solid will rock it all when she falls apart.

In the window there's the garden. There are three birds on the bird table. You can hear their feet pacing and scratching at the wood. You can taste the seeds they're eating, bitter and good. It's almost winter. The sun is paling and cooling, like you. You lift the teacup, shaking, take a sip. It tastes of an empty cup.

It'd come in, slunk through the door, eased into you, letting you slowly out. It all came apart like a peach left for so long to dry and rot its round, plump form turns to dust at the slightest fingertip pressure. Ash. It comes into the room in long bright, sunlit fingers. Your own fingers are an amalgamation of dust. The cup, for example, is far too solid for them to lift. Skin dances in an unchoreographed haze, and breaks occasionally into wounds that have to be swept out and mopped by slippery nurses. They reattach skin to skin with plastic tape, dressings, dust to dust.

She's pouring the tea from the metal canister again. It is another time.

'Do you have children?'

You look at her. Move your lips for speech. There is the boy again, with his black eyes. A gathering in your throat. You're pulling the parts of it together.

She comes closer. Her ear is a seashell, waiting for the sea. Into the shell you whisper.

'Yes,' you say, 'I have a boy. A boy called Isaac.'

'How old is he?'

You shrug, for *don't know.*

She nods again.

'Does he ever come?' she asks.

You nod.

'He's coming soon,' you say.

She frowns a little.

The way she ripples as you breathe.

His black, living eyes.

He holds a cup to your lips, sweet tea, and then, when you've fully drained it, lifts you from the bed like a beach pebble. Putting your small body on the chair, he places your pale feet in a bowl of lake water and washes them. Into the air your silence is light as ash. He opens the big window and the building exhales your last wisp.

Three Poems
Nia Davies

The smithereens

opening
        the mustard seeds
and thinking, how would I organise Saturn & Jupiter?

Open up you can tell the jar.
        But I might not want to.

If I could just give up 'Middle Class'
what expression would that be and would it be useful?

Or if I could just wait here long enough maybe food will be served

my one job today was to water the plant
& pay the people I owe

I do not complete that sentence
because if I do that

I still owe the old man £700

The story of nail clippers, where are they? He is always asking and I owe it to him to find them.

I owe the world no confession, I tell myself

The world does not owe it to you to listen to your confession or anything else, I tell myself.

I owe The Minister for Work and Pensions no information or currency, I tell myself.

Smithereens, from the Irish Smidirín
expresses what exactly

Is to confess a commodity fetish?
Is to express a commodity fetish?

I express my smithereens

'Everyone wants to express themselves' said the man in the tatty church hall when I was trying to be useful.

The plundered do not owe us anything.

I do not owe the bureaucracy my information, I tell myself

I do know how to make the mustard seeds useful and that I am a citizen by accident.

I paid £80 for this passport.

I paid the bureaucracy for proof I am a citizen of a country I was accidently born in

So how would you put Saturn & Jupiter into their proper bureaucratic profit margin?

They do not owe you any gas

My one job today was to water the plant

It is not sufficient to be waiting like this

A cold shoulder of lamb. And when I wheeze
like this you can feel my pollen.

Night-jar hands - I mean that they are cold.

You've been washing in soil again.

And I've become the seventh sea: a waiting child
waiting for a child, waiting for you to be an adult.

The book entitled *Three Ways to MAKE IT*
could be made from any number of perfectly good trees.

The Christmas wreath has not been taken down by us
or anyone else.

You put most latitudes down as *wanting to visit*.

Night-life is a loneliness machine.   ˪

I think of the light shifting from pole to pole through the
year and if you walked
from the Arctic to equator, that would be a long walk but a
good walk.

Medicinal waiting.

Floral waiting
born waiting.

Waiting to not be your mother but someone else's.

What would life as a lawnmower be like?
What would life in the grass be like?

I circle the balustrade once to tell you
I am still waiting. A lamb is white because it is so.

But it can also be brown having been cooked so.

There is kitchen conversation and then there is kitchenette
conversation.

You can have my travel bag full of adapter plugs. My lungs
have also gathered tacky stickers from all of the

visits and the visitations.
It's possible I have the right kind of night.

But I am rotten when I think straight.

About me

Because I was sleeping all over here,
and here. The magnesium intake nightly,
the slosh of the road in the distance.

Heaven had already soiled me.
Who's that scaling the terraced garden?
I opened one eye in the dark,
then someone braver opened both.

I made to swing out of a lime-tree,
said *deepen, foster*. Thought of when I was young,
I would think selkies, think *skerry calf*.

I would listen through lids,
less scathing, less scrape and tangle.
An alarm sounded and everyone ignored it.

Girlgrief
Nuala O'Connor

'How do people in the graveyard get breakfast?'

Her grandad and I look at each other. This is the season of questions.

'Is God made out of sand?' she asks.

Kelly is four years old and we first met her a month ago, in Rättvik, at our son's funeral. Her mother is still in Sweden and no longer cares to raise her daughter.

Kelly watches us leave a room as if we're leaving her life; she sheds no tears and eats little. She says the sourdough I make tastes of socks and walls. We coax preferences from her.

'Lingonberries,' she says.

'Pickled gherkins.'

'Curry and rice.'

We order Indian food and Kelly is pleased.

'Samosa is a type of pudding icing,' she says, 'so yum.'

We nod, baffled, but we're glad that there is food that she lets past her lips.

She calls me Granny and will sit by me in the house and walk beside me in the park, but if I try to hold her hand, she curls away, a coiled fern. Her grandad, she ignores.

I put her to bed in our son's old bedroom, thinking I will have to de-blue it now, for his daughter. I will paint the room yellow to welcome her, unclutter it of hurls and sliotars, the Che Guevara and cannabis posters, the photo-shrine to my son's teenage friends.

Kelly looks around at the grubby remnants of her father's young life.

'We'll buy dolls,' I say, 'and a Noah's ark. We'll get some Lego and a wooden tricycle.'

Kelly sits on the edge of the bed, a rigid statue, and I kneel on the carpet, a supplicant before her.

'When I get married, will *my* husband die?'

'No,' I tell her. 'No, he won't.'

'Actually, he will,' Kelly says. Her seawater eyes dare me to contradict. She glances around the bedroom again and her tone lifts: 'Why did my Daddy have to turn into a magical dead boy? He's gone loco!'

I laugh, thinking this is what she expects, but she lunges forward and thumps my arm with her miniature fist. 'You're so bold!' she screams. She pushes her rage through her nose in spurts and stamps her feet, a tiny, feral horse, railing against her handler.

'Kelly,' I say, 'it's fine to be angry, it's OK to cry. I know you miss your Daddy.' Reluctantly, I add, 'Your Mommy too.'

I sit on the bed beside her and she climbs into my lap and looks up into my face; she puts her hands in mine and with them, I know, all of her faith.

'Cockhorse me to Banbury Cross,' she says, and I do, over and over. 'Horsey, horsey don't you stop,' she commands.

We clippety-clop and tail-swish until my legs ache and my throat is ragged. But I go on and on until she is my son, a jiggling, giddy, four-year-old, who finally tires and lies slack and sated in my arms. I hold Kelly close to my breast and cry into her hair, great sobs gust through me and I shiver. Her arms reach to clasp around my neck.

'Don't cry, Granny,' she says, 'don't cry.'

I sit her back on my knees and look into her face; it thrills me to see her eyes bubble over and the wet soak her cheeks. I pull her to me and rock her and we let our tears wash us clean.

Persephone
Robert Minhinnick

Vipers

Black pantherskins. That's what she saw.

In broken sleep while Ffresni sang to herself, while the child murmured through the hours before dawn and the shadow of the moon-and-stars mobile played over her bed, Nia dreamed of snakes. The bodies of black vipers.

These had been brought out by the weeks of hot weather. So much had been encouraged into the open, adders and orchids unseen for years. Orchid blood on the chalk. Adders dark in her delirium.

Her dream was of vipers. Two fighting snakes were wrapped around one another, two black vipers with tracings of diamonds on their backs, black diamonds on black snakes. Intent and vicious, those vipers.

An Eel in the Fist

Millions of gallons a day, said Nia. And that's not to mention the other resurgences. But where does the water come from?

Some of it riverwater leakage, said Ike. Some of it springwater. Vexes the experts. Hey, I love that word. Vex! So I'm not ashamed to say I'm not sure…

Hallelujah, said Nia. Magic water. Or, water is magic.

I just like the mystery, said Skye. Please don't explain.

We all have to know about this, said Ike. Life and death…You know that Skye.

Of course. I'm taking it seriously. Yes! But I want photographs of somewhere that's never been shot before. We all know safety's vital.

What I meant, said Nia, was that there's enough water. That's for sure. Six million gallons a day usually? And still a lot even in this dry time. That's what I thought when I was in the caving club at college. There's a world we don't see. And it's real. Supporting us. We'd be nothing without it.

They'd reached the new harbour. Serene was ahead holding Ffresni's hand. The pair were finishing a peanut-butter-flavoured ice cream Ike had bought in the fairground. Extra-crunch.

Below on the boardwalks of the jetty a party of anglers was unloading their catch. Already they had the harbour scales outside, plus a measuring tape. Two of the party were holding an enormous fish between them. One of them in waders was putting something in the fish's mouth.

Think…No. Yes. That's a conger, said Ike. Jesus Christ.

They moved down steps to the new quay. Nia told Serene not to bring Ffrez near.

Where'd you catch that? asked Ike.

One of the men looked up. Spat. He was adjusting the cigar he'd positioned in the eel's mouth.

On the reef. Been fishing there thirty years.

Well known, said Ike. Perfect for eels.

Tell us about it, said the fisherman, I've been hearing people talk all my life about one like this. In the end we reeled it in. So far. Then I stopped the boat and we walked it in. Walked it in, I tell you. Top of the reef. Above sea level! It was out of the water, the slimy bastard. Unreal.

I've been over there once, said Ike. There's that lagoon. And the ship's boiler, you can see it from shore. When the sun's on it. Copper, I think. And those caves...

Lot more besides, said the man. My son's a diver and says it's a maze of tunnels under the reef. All unmapped. Perfect for eels. Too narrow for a man...

What about a woman? asked Skye.

Welcome to it, love. Need to be a skinny piece. No turning round. Once you're in you're in.

He and the other angler now had the conger gaffed and chain-hung. Seen this way it was bigger. Maybe ten feet long.

Look at this cunt. Might be forty years old, Teg says. He's over in the office now...

Surprising, said Ike.

The man paused. Gave me a fuckin surprise, I can tell you. We got the daddy here. We got the king. Well, the queen. I'll open its mouth for you. Don't worry, we've finished it off. Can lose fingers, see. Blokes I've known. Or hands.

Smooth, isn't it, said Nia.

Look at those teeth. Jam it open, I will. Jaws on that? Like a cobra. Dislocates, see. Dislocates itself. My son's bringing the other camera. Should be here by now…Be in the papers, this will…This is the daddy.

Maybe female, said Skye.

Well, yeah. This is female. So big, see. Big ones are always…

Yes, said Nia. I've heard the stories…But never thought…Ooh, look at those teeth…

Like the limestone on the reef, said Ike. Daggers.

Just when we copped on, said the fisherman, Teg was talking about the weever fish that's around now. Hot weather, see. Now, they can nip. But nothing like this thing might.

Nia had noted the resurgence of anglers in the town. Yes, it was the extraordinary weather, she thought. And remembered John Vine talking about garfish. Those green garfish on a barbecue near The Horns. Sucking a green bone. Caught in the eelgrass, John Vine had said.

What'll you do? asked Ike.

Sell it. There's no fishmonger around here with a slab big enough. And the scales is too small here. So supermarket boys. Not that eel is popular. Nobody wants eel. Ever bought eel in a restaurant? Would you eat that thing?

Why d'you catch it then? asked Nia.

The fisherman ignored her. Don't worry. It'll go somewhere. They'll cut it. Some kind of fish stew. French name. So we have to take pictures.

The man had put his balled fist into the eel's mouth. Charcoal-grey, that eel. Cold as a lid of ice on a dune slack. Cold as water from The Shwyl. Blood had run out of the conger's mouth. There was a pool of blood on the boardwalk.

With her forefinger Nia traced the eel's skin pattern. There was a glistening brown mixed into the grey and black. Its belly was paler, sulphuric yellow. Or like bark, she thought. Bark of a young tree. More intricate, that pattern the closer she looked into it. Infinite, she thought.

Wish I'd had my bolster, said the angler. Just sharpened it on the grindstone. Could have done with it on the reef.

Something…mythological about this, whispered Skye.

Supermarket? asked Nia. Get an eel in the fist and that's money.

Fist? asked the fisherman. This could have taken my arm off. Still counting fingers.

I mean money's hard to keep hold of. Like an eel. But this is an enormous eel. Like nothing I've ever seen.

Fuckin right, it's big. Maybe the biggest. But it was always there. Waiting. It'll be a YouTube, the boy'll see to that. Be all over Facebook. Filmed it, see. Till it got a bit hairy. We needed every hand free…

The man considered.

Teg's got a lump hammer he uses for sharks. Fuckin four-pounder. Lovely heft. Or fathead, even. Ever seen a real fathead? That's cod to you.

I know, said Nia.

That one the hurricane blew on to the golf course. See that? Showed people how big cod can get. That was on telly.

I was away travelling then, said Ike.

Thornbacks can get biggish, the man continued. Smooth hound the same. Course, that's your small shark. Sea's full of small sharks. Small sharks trying to be big sharks.

But this isn't a shark, said Skye.

Dogfish get big. But never like this. Wait till they see the film in the pub…George'll put it up on screen. Framed picture of me and the boys too. With that thing. I'll make sure of that.

How far you think those tunnels go? asked Ike.

No knowing, is there. Reef seems to be a real mess of gwlis. It's a maze down there. Christ, where's that fuckin camera…

Wouldn't want to come face to face with this, said Nia.

Give you a kiss, love. Pucker up. Nah, they're more scared of you. That's what people say, anyway.

Well…said Nia.

But you're right. Not for me either, love. Wouldn't fancy it at all. Too many corners for me, down in the coldwater coral. I'd rather go shopping than dive under that reef.

You get used to it, said Ike.

Well, Teg better be back really soon. Or this fucker will have smoked his cigar.

The Flying Fox

Isaac Pretty scooped away sand for his shoulder and hip. But he didn't lie down. Instead he threw another driftwood knuckle on the fire. Then a spar, after cracking it in half. He could smell the salt in the wood. Sea pollen, Nia called it.

Some people, he said, referred to it as demolition. Others, the scrap business. Yeah, I was a scrappie. A *tatterman*. Big things. Enormous. Once I worked on an aeroplane. All that insulation, all that plastic. Up in smoke. Incredible. Couldn't do it now...

No, said a muffled voice in the dark. It might have been a question.

And a ship once, not far from here. Maybe one thousand tonnes, that ship. Where those scrapyards go down to the sands. Orchard Levels they call it. And we were taking that ship apart. Eight of us unscrewing, unbolting. Unriveting when we could. Boy, the size of those wrenches we were using. But if the rivets had seized we'd cut.

And four, just four, with cutting gear. I loved the lance they taught me to use. Yeah, that oxyacetylene lance, its flame from yellow to invisible. That was when it was hottest. Could cut a man in half and no one would know. Yes, hottest when it cut through the thousand metal bits we needed to...*dismantle*. Down in the hold in the dark. It was a cave in there. Dripping, dank. A real cave, that hold.

Then I'd climb below the hold. Bilge sludge under my feet. Thick on the walls. Oh yeah, the cave under the cave. Those taps and pumps. We cut them all out. And just the eight of us, taking a ship apart. That oxy smell in my hair and clothes. And always in the air. Never got rid of it.

Sometimes it was just me. Down there, I mean. Weird shadows. But mainly pitch dark. And my own shadow in the spotlights. Just him and me. Like in this firelight.

And weird echoes. You know that hollow sound at the bottom of a ship? Sometimes I slept there to save money and time. Used to fall into my blankets, big suck of whisky, and it would be morning. Time to start all over again. With another slug if I could stomach it. I was at it by four. No, five most days. Because sometimes I had two sucks of that Jura. Yeah, always Jura. Thought it tasted of peatwater. And hot as hell, burn of a burn. Kept me alive. And music in the bilge. Deep under the deck with a stack of old cassette tapes. Ever hear the MC5? Hey, anyone? Out there?

No, said Skye's voice.

Discovered the MC5 from this bloke who was with me on the oxy. Used to turn the tape to max and play one song over and over. *Kick out the Jams, Motherfuckers.* Heard it?

No, said Skye. Thank God.

Mad music. Madmen's music. Just us down in the dark. In the bilge. Spotlights like I say giving these shadows and that song echoing off the metal walls. And me and this real head case, this real motherfucker, screaming down there in the dark. He was older than me. *Sinbad* they called him. He was a punk rocker, no, a real one, knocking on a bit, yeah, but his hair was still dyed manky red. Yeah, Sinbad. He was earning a fortune, must have been. Told me I was lucky to be working with him. Learning off him. Now I know that was true.

You know, sometimes it felt like we were a mile underwater. Just me and Sinbad. Us and the MC5. That Fred Sonic Smith, now there was a guitarist. Greatest recording studio ever, that hold. Fred would have loved it. His godalmighty racket bouncing off the bulkhead. Died of cancer, didn't he?

Shame, said Skye's voice from the dark.

Once, Sinbad and I went to the Red House. Think it's closed now. The Red House?

No idea, said Skye's voice.

Now Sinbad, he took his work seriously. But every now and then he'd fancy a break from routine. And Christ, you should have seen what he could put away. Got into an argument about music in the pub. Didn't like it, did he? Other people's bad music in public. Thought it said something about a man. Badge of honour. Like your soul was on display.

Probably got an iPod now, eh? murmured Skye.

If he's still with us. But MC5? That says it all about Sinbad's taste. Not a man to cross.

Obviously.

Glaswegian. Came from a place called Auchenshuggle. He spelled it for me. Born on the day the last tram ran. Never understood a word he said...

You were probably deaf.

Yeah. That was Sinbad. Piercings all over his face. His *fishooks* he called them.

31

Takes all sorts.

Just us with those lances. Cut you in half, those burning bars. Their invisible flames.

Charming, said Nia. What's the word?

Catharsis? said Skye.

Don't knock it, said Ike Pretty. Had to be done. I'd never used oxy before. Got the scars to prove it. Christ, we broke every rule. And one rivet at a time, remember. That's when I got used to masks and breathing through tubes. How I learned not to be scared of the dark. And if you'd been in the bilge for two months with Sinbad you...

Sounds like a prison term, said Skye.

As I say, I learned. Never stopped. Then later, it turns out I'm in a cave in the Philippines, just looking, only looking, and the guide, a local kid, points out the flying foxes roosting in the roof.

Foxes? said Nia from the dark.

Kind of bat. Big buggers, those flying foxes. Very big. Wings like funeral crepe.

Won't be any in...

No, course not. Might be bats, though. That's normal for caves. Thick as soot, bats. And think of their shit. Thousands of years of batshit. But it all came back to me in that cave in the Philippines. The ship was called *The Flying Fox*. Sinbad's ship. Don't know why. Strange name for a ship, but it made me think...

About? asked Skye.

About how everything comes back, said Ike slowly. No matter how far it travels. Look, here's me, back on The Caib. After I swore it wouldn't happen…

But you had to go first? asked Nia. Didn't you? And now you've been everywhere….

That's why you're invited, said Skye. We feel we're in good hands…

Three Poems
Mari Ellis Dunning

A mind; shifting

Time wrapped its fat hands around my grandmother's brain,
held it steady in its grasp and squeezed. Her mind, once a dining room
of fine china, teacups and porcelain cavaliers, now a street bazaar,
her treasures strewn, for sale, amongst nick-nacks,
plastic toys and choking hazards.

She knew me still, but only as a child; she asked if I had been left
in the car, said I was too young to be out there alone. The little girl
she spoke of, the one curled like a crab inside my gut,
called out to her, pounding on my eyeballs
until they stung.

Time shrunk my grandmother's brain, used powerful fists
to drain the juice from it, leaving only pulp behind,
until she didn't know her own surroundings; though she held
fast her penchant for sweetened tea and a stiff upper lip.

She told me once about a trip to town, accompanied by her own
mother. I could taste the crumbs of their afternoon tea on my lips
when she was done describing it, and I wondered if she had dreamt,

imagined, or remembered that speckled scone,
buttered and split between two.

While her thin eyelids flickered like rice paper, and her head lay
on plastic pillows, she was caught somewhere between the black sea
and the dying stars. Those shrivelled grey cells, a key
to another universe.

Moulded to her armchair like brown-red clay ready for the kiln,
I see her still, dancing through a place in which her mother
lives, still; a place in which her legs bounce, still wrapped
in stockings, and where I am a child, still.

Time took my grandmother's brain tissue and rolled it between
thumb and index finger, like a fascinated child examining a bug.
I watched as her mind drained like an overused battery,
saw the clothes grow bigger around her waist while her calves
swelled like fat frogs.

You toss aside your pitying looks, mumble your apologies,
but Time stretches out its arms, wraps them like cords around
our necks and calls us all back, into the past. I see her now,
her smile reverberating like violin string as she exists
in a shifting world of her own creation.

Reaching

As thick drapes shut out the world,
Trapping cold air and shadows
in tightly-wound fabric,
I fell asleep
with a fish bone in my throat.
Darkness filled the corners of the room
 and it lodged
an iron bolt
blocking the vowels and consonants,
the sleepy syllables from pushing through my chest
and out of my dry lips - -

I couldn't reach for you through the darkness.

There has been an emptiness in me;
I have felt its wings scratch at my chest,
Felt it curl and consort with the yellow bile of my stomach.
As the sun crosses the sky
and sets over still water,
I take no comfort in that fresh salt smell - -

Only sickness settles within me now - -

And still, I can't reach for you.

Days stretch endlessly before me,
I am pulled, stumbling, through their shadows,
The seed still deep within my skull.
Black tendrils spiral from the crown of my head,
Fall like running water and wrap me in their thorn-grip,
  sprouting   sprouting
        shooting
Pinning my arms to my sides
and trapping my tongue - -

So I can't reach for you.

Oystermouth

the night swallowed the sand grains
wet as oil and tepid,
it spun like a reel of film
far across the horizon
and out of sight,
gone.

I remember walking hand in hand
with you,
swaddled from the light rain
which drizzled and misted
and wrapped us up
like parcels,

and we danced when our footfalls
sunk
into the sand
and the sea laughed at us

and the gulls that should
have been circling overhead
were gone too,
their heads tucked under wings,
silent as the names we wrote
on pressed paper

earlier that same day.

the darkness pressed itself
around us,
hungry as a walrus,
it devoured the trumpet shaped shells
and left us tinkering
on the precipice of an oyster's mouth,
wide and gaping
and waiting
for tomorrow.

Feathering the Blade
Emily Devane

'Fast catches for ten! One, two, three…'

Mel's voice, calm as an airline pilot's, rings out over the mic. We got here early to practise for the 2k sprint. It's the crew's first race from a standing start and there's a chill in the air, the spring sky a cool blue.

'…Four, five, six…'

With each stroke, my thigh muscles burn. I slide forward – seven, eight. There's a pain in my lungs, my heart. There's a husky catch to her words from too many cigarettes. What I wouldn't do for that voice – even after everything.

'…Nine, ten. That's it! Wind it up, now. Keep going!'

Facing us from her perch in the stern, Mel keeps time. She's tiny compared with the men in the boat – and yet, at her command, eight oars clunk against eight metal gates, eight wrists flatten eight blades, making them glide low above the water, like feathers. She oversees the mechanical whoosh of eight slides, seats moving forwards, legs bent, knees over shoes: eight sets of coiled springs. Breaths in, breaths out. A softer clunk, as our oars rotate once more, arms stretched wide over riggers, blades sliced into water, quick as the heads of bobbing ducks. Legs pushing away, wrists pulling through. Our muscles burn from it: the pushing and pulling and twisting. Blood pulses behind our ears. Sweat drips into our open mouths, leaving the tang of salt. Then it begins again. She's the conductor of her very own waterborne orchestra:

Clunk. Whoosh. Clunk. Slice. Push. Clunk. Whoosh. Clunk. Slice. Push.

'And there.' A satisfied clip to her words. The boat seems to lift; everything working together. This is when it's easy. I fix my eyes on Stroke's neck in front; the muscular German with beads of sweat at the base of his hairline; his body a piston, leader of the mechanical orchestra. Doing Mel's bidding, his face just inches from hers at full stretch, he sets the pace for the rest of us to follow. He's bigger than me by half.

'Much better. So much better on those finishes, guys. Easy oars,' Mel says. We push our arms away once more, leaving our blades feathered. The water glides noiselessly beneath them.

Then, above the quiet, a flapping sound starts up. Beyond Mel's seat, I watch a lone swan flying low to the water like our feathered blades, beating its wings against the boat's settling wake. He's big – 11lb at least – and he's all puffed up, the mighty muscles of his wings drawn back, dragging his black feet in the water, wings slapping down hard, again and again. He cruises to a stop and treads water, watching us with kohl-black eyes set in a permanent frown.

'Crazy swan!' Stroke says, swiping his oar through the air. 'Back off!'

Stroke's shouting sets the bird off again. He rises up, breast thrust forward, drumming his wings against the water and I see his

41

beak, its ridged edges like a line of teeth, pin sharp. He's full of testosterone, no different from the eight panting men in our boat. Except this is the swan's territory and he wants us gone.

'Let's get out of here,' I shout over Stroke's shoulder, trying to catch Mel's eye. I can't help but notice her hair. It looks so lovely in this light, as if it's all aflame. 'You okay?'

Though she nods, her eyes don't quite meet mine. There's something wrong, I can sense it.

'Mel?'

'I'm okay. He clipped me, that's all.' She touches the early bloom of a bruise on her cheek.

Coach calls out from the riverbank. We'll turn, go back to the lock, he tells us. Nev's a third-year medic, a man of few words but an experienced rower. Not many win their oars in their very first term.

'Okay. Backing down, bow-side.' Mel's voice crackles through the mic.

With my eyes on the swan, I lead the bow-side men. Stroke's neck muscles twitch in front of me. Adrenalin or irritation, it's hard to say which. While the stroke-side men sit motionless, we tap our blades through the water to turn the boat, feeling the stretch of it as the boat spins. The bird's cruising among the reeds at the riverbank, returning my gaze. My stomach's churning and my mouth tastes sour. I drank too much last night.

'I don't like the look of him,' Stroke says. He rubs the sweat from his neck with his free hand.

'Maybe he's taken a liking to you, Melder?' I can't place the voice from the bow but the next comment riles me: 'You should challenge it to a duel, Matty!' Always some smart-arse joke. I've learned to ignore them.

Mel's voice sounds weird. 'Ha, ha. Very funny.' She whispers something under her breath, something that only Stroke can hear. Then, louder, she says: 'We need to get a shift on, guys. Race starts in half an hour.' She hates being called Melder. It's an old Cornish name, I looked it up. It means sweet as honey. Maybe that's the bit she objects to.

We paddle steadily, conserving energy for the race. The river's getting busy. Spectators mill about on the riverbank while on the towpath, coaches jostle for position on wobbling bikes, struggling to be heard over the noise. Marshals in high-vis jackets hold flags and clipboards, checking their lists of crews – distinguishable by the colour of their Lycra vests and matching blades. Slowing to negotiate a bottleneck, we see a crew pass by in pink and brown.

'Those guys look like pigs in shit!'

Mel's not in the mood: 'Eyes in the boat, Stroke!'

The German turns to me with a face of mock fear. 'It's Matty you want to watch,' he says. If he wasn't holding an oar, I would punch his stupid face.

Then, from his motor boat, the umpire raises the loudhailer to his mouth. 'Cromwell, Fairbairn, St Mary's, Christ's, Meldrick. To the start line, please.'

'You're quite discerning, aren't you Matty?' Stroke continues, as we row to the start line. 'About the women you like to watch.' The way he says it is kind of creepy: quiet, so that Mel can't hear. It sounds like a threat.

'Shut it.' I hiss, wondering what he knows, what she's told him.

We were on alcohol ban last night, although there was some party in the bar. I was a few pints down when I made for the exit, steadying myself with one hand on the wall, and stumbled into Mel coming the other way, dress riding up her knickers, hair undone. 'What are you staring at?' she growled.

'Just looking.'

'You're always "*just looking*", Matty. Just looking! Makes me sick, makes me sick!' She glared at a passing third-year. 'The lot of you!'

Just a few beers. Promised myself I'd stop early. Except I didn't. After Mel had run at me, pushed me so that I fell into the path of some second-year guy who threatened to *punch my stupid boaty brains out*, I went back to the bar and ordered beers with whisky chasers. Bad idea.

Melder was the girl on the Freshers photo that all the second-years pored over. Pawed over, more like. She became *that* girl, the one we all wanted. She, meanwhile, was strangely unmoved by our interest.

One day I overheard her talking about an exhibition. When she got to the museum, I was sitting on a bench made out of a single curved piece of wood, as if I did this kind of thing every day. I had a notebook open on my knee and was attempting a sketch.

'See this?' She stood beside the bronze sculpture of the big-buttocked woman with tendrils of hair covering her naked chest, some sort of bird's wing wrapped around her thigh, its neck stretched towards her face, a winged cupid at her side.

'Nice pet,' I said, not knowing what I was supposed to say. She'd never spoken to me before.

'Do you recognise it?'

'Should I?'

'You've never read Yeats?'

'Erm, no.'

'It's *Leda and the Swan*.'

'I see.'

'But do you?'

'I think so.'

'Some people think she wanted it, she was looking for it.' She pointed at Leda's face. Her bronze lips were parted into a coy smile.

I've never been good at faces. It's taken me years to figure them out, to recognise what's being meant; so often it's different from what's being said. I studied that smile for some time. There was something about it – something *knowing*.

'But what woman in her right mind would want *that*?' Mel circled the three bronze figures, finally bending to examine the claw embedded in Leda's flesh.

'Exactly,' I said, not understanding, not fully. By this time, she'd moved on to a naked centaur. Later, I looked up the poem in the library. Did that change things? That the swan was in fact a man? Did it make it more dignified, somehow? I wondered if she meant to warn me, was trying to tell me to stay away.

I started rowing because of her. That way, I would get to see her every day – even if Stroke ruined the view. I began to wait for her by the towpath, offered to walk her home. She was usually busy but she sometimes said yes.

One time, I bought her a drink in the bar. 'You're a gent, Matty! How did you know cider was my favourite? And a pint, too. Cheers!' She took the glass and clinked it with mine. Her smile was open; an invitation – I was sure that's what it was. But when I moved closer, put my hand on her leg, she moved it away.

'You mislaid this?' She spoke coolly, giving back my hand. *That hand stays there, with you*, was what she really meant. I thought about it for a while. I came to wondering if maybe it meant *yes – bu, not here.*

Last night, after the whisky, I made my way to her room, just to say goodnight away from everyone else. A kiss, perhaps. Nothing more.

She opened the door and slapped my face.

I stood there dumbly. She looked so young, standing there in her Winnie The Pooh pyjamas.

'You, you, you!' she yelled. 'Stay away from me! Stay away! I don't want you near me. You, or anyone else.'

That's when I reached for her face. I wanted to make things better. A stupid thing to do, I now realise. Too late I saw, at the base of her neck, a bruise. On her arm, a cluster of red marks, as if she'd been hugged too tight and not let go.

'Please, Matty. Please just go.'

The gun goes off, the sound bouncing off the water. We begin. Quarter slide, half slide, three quarters slide. Winding up to full pace, like going through the gearbox from first to fifth. Her voice is edged with a shot of adrenalin. My lungs ache. Vomit floods my mouth. Sliding forwards and backwards, my ears fill with sounds: *Clunk. Whoosh. Clunk. Slice. Push. Clunk. Whoosh. Clunk. Slice. Push.* We're ahead, ahead. Keep. Going. Keep. Going. That's the spirit, that's the flavour. Then someone digs too deep. Blades are going everywhere and it's messy, choppy. And the boat's careening towards the bank, and we're way too near, way too near to the bank, so near that I'm brushing against earth. I pull my blade in, push against the bank, hold it straight and we start again. Quarter slide, half slide, three quarters slide, gaining momentum. The other boats' bows are getting closer. Wind it up, quick finishes – there! And there! But we're still too close to the bank and the boat behind us is pulling alongside, its bowman moving past me.

'Come on, Cromwell! Final push. The finish is in sight!' It's coach Nev, calling from his bike. I slam my legs down hard, pull a little harder on the finish – but it's still sloppy. The boat lurches left and right. We're an orchestra out of time. Someone on stroke side is digging too deep, sending the boat off balance.

'Cox, move away from the bank!' the umpire's voice yells through the loudhailer. We're nearing the finish. 'Cox, move away!'

'I'm trying!' screams Mel, but there's something wrong. 'Bow, big strokes now. Lighter from stroke side.'

As I slide forward, I see her mouth hinged wide, unable to form the words to make us stop. Too late, too late. I can't see what she can see. She's the eyes, after all; we're just travelling backwards, blindly.

The boat begins to lift and we're picking up speed, following Stroke's oblivious rhythm. I don't see it happen, only the aftermath – the blood on the tip of my blade. Sliding forward, low to the water, my oar skims through the air, slips into the water and out. We're flying now, really flying. One last push for the finish when the blade hits something, goes straight through, like a scythe through corn. Too late, too late.

We row on – what else is there to do? Hands trembling, I watch the floating mass of white bobbing up and down in the boat's wake. The bird's gullet, cut cleanly at the neck. I see the neck lying among the reeds; his indifferent beak, like the handle of an umbrella in some novelty shop. I look at my oar, the blood on my blade, and I retch.

She screams as we cross the finish line: 'That's it! Keep going!' The other crew is a vague blur alongside us. *Have we won?*

Someone asks. Mel doesn't look back. She stares ahead, her mouth still open. I can hear her gasping over the microphone, as if she's catching up on lost breaths. And that's when I see it. Something about her mouth, the way her lips are parted. The slight smile at a job well done. I look at the blood, plain to see on my blade, then my eyes go back to that smile. *Some people think she wanted it, she was looking for it.*

Right now, with the morning sun resting on her bronze hair, she's at her most beautiful. Right now, she's so terribly, shamelessly beautiful, that I have to look away.

Fango in the Mire
Derwen Morfayel

'How many days since you last showered?' you ask.

'Day before yesterday,' Tegan replies. She raises her mug to her lips, pretending to drink the tea that is no longer there. 'What? So I don't shower every day. It isn't supposed to be a daily thing, you know. It's actually not good for skin, over-washing it.'

'Okay, what about changing your clothes?'

'I have.'

'No, you haven't,' you remind her, pulling the face you use when she tells you she has woken up after noon or missed a deadline at work. You reach out for a biscuit from the table between you. 'Love, I mean it. Change your underwear, at least.'

'Shush.' Tegan turns up the volume of the television, where Jeremy Kyle is having a go at someone, a young guy whose story you haven't been listening to. 'They're doing the paternity test in a minute.' She rests her head on the arm of the lounge chair and hugs the remote as though it is a teddy bear. Her roots are showing, growing out into the red.

You gaze at the screen until Jeremy says '...is NOT the father...' and the young guy walks off after telling the girl to *bleep* herself.

When the adverts are on, you say, 'Blue, lacy, with a little rose in the middle.'

'Hm?'

'I bet you those are the knickers you're wearing right now.' You stick a finger behind the elastic of her pyjama bottoms and fish out the blue briefs. The rubber plaque at the back reads *La Senza* and under her navel is the tiny red rose.

'All right, don't give me a wedgie.' She wiggles your hand away.

'And you were wearing them four days ago, I remember because it was the night you fell asleep right where you're sitting now and I put you to bed, changed your clothes.'

'Perve.' She smiles and gets up to clear the coffee table. 'There was no need to undress me,' she says, squeezing the two used teabags inside their napkins and placing them in your empty mugs.

'Right, that's it.' You quickly get up and tug at her dressing gown.

'Get off!'

You untie the bow of her pyjama bottoms and they fall to her ankles with ease. 'Arms up,' you say. 'Clothes are coming off.'

Tegan jokes even though she knows you don't mean sex. 'Not even a cocktail first.' She steps out of her bottoms and lifts up her arms like an obedient child ready for a bath. Her palms face forward in a gesture of surrender. 'I guess I thought…yeah, it must've been a few more days then.' She sniffs her armpit.

You remove her Disney top and hold it up to check for stains. Lady the cocker spaniel is smiling from the crumpled 100% cotton T-shirt. Its tag says it is for people aged eight to nine years. Tegan is twenty-eight.

'Do I smell?' she asks.

'Put it this way,' you say, 'when I bought you these pyjamas I should've chosen the ones with Tramp's face instead.'

*

You sit in front of the washing machine watching the clothes tumble inside the silver basket. You are mentally counting all the odd socks you found under the bed and thinking of where their lost pairs could be. Fango your Labrador sits by your side with his tongue out. Every now and then he wags his tail at thin air.

He enjoys playing with the ghosts of the house, you often say to Tegan.

Tegan is in the bath zapping through the Queen playlist on her phone. She sings along and laughs when she fails at the falsetto voices.

You get up to pencil in a smiley face in today's box on the RSPCA calendar on the fridge. There are a few sad faces this month but no serious ones, not since you last argued. When was it? You flick back the pages and skim the boxes full of gym sessions and doctor's appointments and shopping reminders. There it is in September. That was when you last talked about babies. It is the same conversation, over and over again: you remind her of the children waiting to be adopted in the world and all she hears is that you don't want a sperm donor. She knows how you feel about it, but the truth is she wouldn't cope with pregnancy. You don't tell her that, of course, because last time you did, it led to the serious face on the calendar. You turn its pages back to the black puppies of December.

You begin to draw the smiley face but you don't finish it.

Only the two dots, its eyes, are there.

There is no smile, there are no lips.

It is staring at you, mouthless.

The pencil is not in your hand any more.

You look down.

It is on the floor even though you didn't hear it fall. You can't hear anything now.

Breathing is hard.

It is happening again. What started it this time?

Think.

No, breathe.

Your abdomen is beating with pulse and filling and falling with breath and yet it brings no relief, in much the same way as a yawn interrupted. Invisible earmuffs block out all noise. You lean your forehead against the fridge and wait for the volume of the world to rise.

Gradually, you hear the cord of the neighbour's washing line being pulled, Tegan's music and her voice humming through the wall, dog claws against the kitchen tiles.

You kiss the air to call Fango. He steps carefully around the breakfast table, barred for a moment by the scent of Tegan's empty slippers before finding you and sniffing your knee.

'We're going for a walk,' you tell him, but for a while you stay there, holding his snout in your hands.

From within the folds of his black mouth, Fango's spit dribbles out. His fur is the shade of Tegan's real hair, the colour of wheat, and his eyes that were once brown are now white in places, discoloured, bleached of sight.

'Not even *you* see me, boy,' you whisper.

*

Having walked a few blocks, you stop outside a small shop to buy chocolate; sugar might do you good. Through the window you see a bar of Snickers with your name on it. The dark-haired man behind the counter points at the bicycle racks by the door. He is silently telling you, with a smile, to leave your four-legged companion outside.

You make a knot around the metal bars with the dog leash and pat Fango's head. He thinks you are on your way to the park, but he knows you are taking too long and that this street and the piss on its pavements do not smell familiar.

The shopkeeper is with a little girl you think must be his daughter. You nod as you enter, suddenly immersed in trying to work out how many slices of bread are left and whether there will be enough fruit to last until the end of the week. Before getting to the counter, you glance at the fridges, wondering about the expiry date of the milk back home. What if, just this once, you bought a bottle with a blue cap? The one you prefer. The answers to your 'what ifs' tend to be the same: Tegan might cry. You even wonder what would happen if, once you left the shop, you simply carried on walking.

You might not get far with the two pounds, ten pence change that jingles next to the keys in your pocket, but you could walk to your brother's house and he would lend you money. Once you tell him what is wrong, he could comb your hair like when you were little and you would fall asleep in your old room, ready for a new life tomorrow.

'You alright there?' the shopkeeper is saying.

You are standing still in front of the milk fridge, palm against the glass sliding door as though reaching out to a loved one on the other side.

The girl giggles into her hands and goes to open the fridge you have been watching. You think she is laughing at you.

'I forgot my shopping list,' you say, 'I was trying to remember it.'

The girl looks up at you. Her eyes are grey and they make you think of a time when you smiled every day and jumped in puddles instead of dodging them, splashing about with stamping feet in bright blue wellies.

You see the carton boxes of tampons and you know you need to stock up because you saw it noted down in the calendar, *DUE!* in red pen.

It is now you realise why it was you couldn't breathe properly.

Both of your lives are summarised in that calendar, 'Today is a good day', 'Today is a bad day', 'Today is an in-between day', and absolutely everything was in your handwriting.

You grab a box of the tampon brand that sounds the softest, remembering that you also bleed, that you too are a woman and, although sometimes you forget, you too are alive.

*

You can smell Fango's wet fur. He knows you are definitely not going to the park.

Your brother will think you a coward, but it is not as if you would be leaving Tegan alone. She may have lost many friends over the years but she still has her family, her parents. They have always been around, it was the two of you who caved yourselves in your flat. That is what Tegan did and slowly you did it too. You began to ignore the phones and the doorbell and said no to plans. Even your periods synched.

You would never have anticipated this hermit life. She was different when you met her, wasn't she? The first thing you saw of Tegan was her head of scruffy hair at a party. A halo of light shone on it from some neon lamp that made her caramel highlights appear to be spilling like syrup on an ice cream. Yes, that is Tegan – a dollop of fresh fluffy cream turned stale. And so began this dependency, this terrible, terrible love. Tegan is loveable and breakable as an old china-faced doll. But you never said 'in sickness and in health'.

Thunder rumbles and the clouds ignite. The dog leash tightens and you must pull Fango along. It feels cruel to do that when his ears are pointing back, surrendering under the storm. Your palms are lined with the leash's handle the way they redden with heavy plastic shopping bags. Briefly and repeatedly, the flashes of the sky's camera illuminate Fango's white eyes with lightning.

Fango does not want to keep walking and you grow tired of tugging. He sits on trembling limbs, yelping. You kneel, feeling the rainfall soak your denim knees. You cover him, hold him, shush him. His fur has flattened and you can't brush through it with your fingers. It feels like leather.

'I'm here,' you tell him, with a hand on the scruff of his neck and your forehead between his eyes.

To leave would mean taking Fango with you; Tegan can't handle the responsibility, she wouldn't walk him because she hates leaving the house and he would end up fat. Besides, Fango is your boy. She doesn't deserve to keep him. It was you who found him squealing in that garbage bin surrounded by dead brothers. *You* saved him and raised him, gave him milk from a tiny bottle, rubbed his bum to teach him to poo. Fango loves Tegan, but he worships *you*, the furless mother. He knew no other and so he thinks the teat that fed him was yours.

But how would he cope? Memory is everything for him to feel at home. He knows exactly where the litter is, where to turn corners and how to dodge the furniture, the width of the rooms. He has counted the steps from the front door to his bed under the kitchen sink. His scent has been rubbed and licked and wagged everywhere. Starting again would be frustrating at his age. You can't go.

You have to stay, for him.

*

Retracing your steps, your stride is slow but Fango is speeding up. Once he can smell his paws and your trainers on the pavement, he knows it is the road travelled and that you are going home. His tail comes out from between his legs. You follow the cord of the leash to his neck and press down on the spring of the snap hook. You even remove the collar, because you like him better that way. His collar binds him to your name, to that house. It is his chain. For a moment, you wish that he were free, so you could be too.

The evening sky is still groaning but Fango's yelping has stopped. His head is high. He turns back to check you are near. How does he know? Then he is off again, blind and confident as a child skipping in the rain.

The handle of his leash stays in your hand, light.

Three Poems
Niall Griffiths

In a Hospital the Size of a Small Town

he lay on the bed naked
hairy giblets on show
he's dying said his family
& I said don't worry
does he want some tea
fuck off with your tea he said &
he's dying said his family
don't worry I said

she was reading The Lover
& so was I
her left arm caused her agony because
it was the only part of her not cancerous
I miss my horses she said
milk no sugar
one day we'll ride together

I was in Crete he said

my granddad too I said
I'll never forgive them he said
I'll hate them til I die
he laughed then
& looked out of the window
his slippers had a crest on the toes
those Nazi bastards

the ward smelled of dinners
& the chemicals beneath
I scraped the leftovers into a binbag
stacked the trolley in the lift
and pressed LG

in the catheter pipes the blood-clots shoaled
in the kidney bowls sat stuff
uniforms dashed and curtains were pulled
so that death could be met in secret

& I poured the tea &
I gathered plates & cups
around in the big brown building
humans & their vast machinery
tried to keep other humans alive

sun rose, sun set
beyond this building horses ran

the sky was filled with fear & flame
& beyond that building horses ran
men dismembered men &
love was doomed to die

I poured the tea &
I handed out the food &
I scraped the scraps into binbags &
I earned the fare back home

Polish Beer (I Mean Beer from Poland)

It's an effective test – the
anthology of modern poetry & the
bottles of Tyskie & Brok
in the June garden. Can
the first sustain an interest
whilst you consume the second
without you wanting to only
look at the authors' portraits?

Motherhood: travel: memory: the
illness of a family member:
momentary revelations of what a bird in flight
means to the self.

& so it quietly comes to this – she
looks like she'd rather be baking cakes. She
looks like she'd rather be gardening. He
looks like he's worried that he looks like his father.
And HIM, well, he looks like he's made of dough
and been left out to dry
in a very humid region of the world.

Student Nurse

Use more active verbs, I tell her,
& she tells me about
the guy with the roll-on deodorant up his anus.

You're telling too much, I said, & don't tell but show,
& she tells me how she had to reach inside
& unscrew the tube
but the lid remained within.

I told her that the typography was all over the place, & to
look at how other writers, published writers,
lay dialogue out on the page. She
tells me about the old man who
leaned back onto the broom-stick & slipped
& was brought in choking on
his own vomited excrement.

A semi-colon is not a comma, I said.
She said they had to break the Marmite jar with a hammer,
gently, tap-tap-tapping against the thick glass to
free the trapped testicles.

Letters Above the Door
Neil Campbell

As I walked in for the interview, I noticed a half empty glass of water on the table, left by the previous candidate. There were marks of her breath on the glass. Sitting down, I looked at the water again, but nobody on the panel moved. There were three academics: a woman, with a huge and justifiable chip on her shoulder about the marginalisation of women in literature, and two men. One of these men seemed to be impressed by everything I said. He was red faced and amiable. After my presentation, the woman, itching for intellectual debate, said, 'What elevates this to master's level?' Later, the other man on the panel said, with something approaching a sneer, 'How do you situate yourself in the contemporary field?'

Afterwards I walked down to Princes Street. Waiting at a pedestrian crossing I watched as the crowd of shoppers piled up on the other side, massing in the morning sunshine. My shirt was stained with sweat. I sat down on a bench in the shadow of the castle. Before the interview I'd googled the people on the panel. As far as I could tell, none of them had had any creative work published.

I dropped into Debenhams with the vague intention of buying a new shirt. There were escalators and stairs among the white shining walls. Arrows pointed to 'Menswear', but after some fifteen minutes of walking I found myself in a cul-de-sac of suitcases. I started to walk more quickly and found myself back in a place I'd seen before, a corner of the store displaying shoes.

'How do I get out?' I said, to a middle-aged man standing by a tiny glass lift. 'I can't get out.'

'Oh I know, it's terrible, I've known people stuck in here for days.'

Eventually I walked out onto the blazing street. The walls of the castle glinted in the sun. I weaved my way through the tumult of people rushing for meal deals. I turned down a side street and walked along a quiet, cobbled road. There was a man standing outside a pub, smoking a thin cigar. 'Just go in,' he said, smiling.

There was the bar, with six stools before it, and two sets of window seats with room for two people in each. Three of the stools were occupied, and a tall barman, the landlord, stood behind the counter, smiling. To the side of the bar there were wooden steps leading to a side room with tables. I had a look in there before deciding on a stool. I asked for a pint of Best and then perched myself at the end of the bar, near the window.

I sat quietly, listening to the sporadic conversation. When tourists came in, the bar came to life with a series of questions:

'Is this the Rebus place?'

'Is Ian in?'

'Is he coming in later?'

'We want to try whisky. What do you recommend?'

'Is this a smooth whisky?'

'Do you have water, in it? Ice? How much?'

'Are single malts better?'

One American couple stayed a while, but when the man pointed his huge camera at the landlord and the locals they covered their faces and turned away in mock horror.

The landlord had sky blue eyes and a red nose. His shirt sleeves were rolled to the forearms and he pulled pints with big hands. He was a Celtic fan, and they'd lost a European tie to a bunch of part-timers the night before.

'Hey, Harry, at least in the next leg your boys will be able to get their gas boilers checked out, eh?' said a little bloke called Alan, sitting on one of the other stools. 'No like the mighty Hibs!'

'I see Lennon's got banned already,' I said.

'Oh aye,' said Alan.

'I'm a Man City fan.'

'Oh, you're from Manchester? I went there once. Just the once,' said Harry, with a wry smile.

'I came for an interview at the university. Creative Writing,' I said.

'Oh right?'

'So I'm doing the literary pilgrimage.'

'You been to Milne's?'

'No, where's that?'

'Just on Hanover Street there.'

'That where MacCaig and them went?'

'Aye. But it's no like it was. There used to be loads of photographs and everything. I used to run it. It's changed now. But they've still got the Little Kremlin. Sorley Maclean, all of them used to sit in there and *orate*.'

'MacCaig was my primary school teacher,' said the man who had been smoking the thin cigar outside. He was called Kenny.

'Always had a glint in his eye when you saw him interviewed,' I said.

'Aye he did. That's because he was always pished,' said Harry.

'No, not always. But you're right, he liked a wee dram and a fag. And he did have a glint in his eye,' said Kenny.

'You know a pub called The Circus?' said Harry.

'Circus Tavern?' I said.

'That's right.'

'We're kind of twinned with that place. I went there once.'

'Tiny place. Smaller than this.'

'Oh aye. But they still had a corner there they called a snug. It was incredible.'

'It's about the size of this room.'

'That's right.'

'I taught at Salford Uni. There's another good boozer there. The Crescent. Marx and Engels went in.'

'Dirty Old Town. Used to sing that when I knew Gerry.'

'Who's this fella?' I asked.

'Gerry Rafferty,' said Kenny.

'Oh aye,' said Alan.

'Baker Street,' I said.

'He sang with Billy,' said Kenny. 'The bumbleheads or something.'

'The Bumblebees,' said Alan.

'No the Humble Bumbles,' said Kenny.

'The humbumbles, oh, something like that. We sang on the same bill sometimes. Gerry was a nice fella.'

'I left my heart, by the gasworks wall, dreamed a dream, by the old canal…' it was Harry again, singing the lyrics of Ewan McColl.

Just then a couple of tourists came in. 'Do you do fish and chips here?' they asked Harry.

'Used to. But we stopped the food,' he said.

'Oh. But how does fish and chips work?'

'How does it *work*?'

'You put it on the plate? You could try Milne's if you like, they do food over there.'

As they left, Harry bid them a fond farewell. 'How does it *fucking work*?' he said, turning to the regulars.

'So that's him up on the wall then?' I said, as the mild laughter subsided.

'Aye. But you see that John Hannah? He was shite in the role compared to the bloke Stott that came after. But you know Hannah bought shares in it all. He's no fucking stupid,' said Alan.

'Yeah, Ian bought the shares back I think. Few years ago,' said Harry.

'I've never really watched it. Canongate's from here though, isn't it?' I said.

'That's right, aye. I knew the fella set that place up,' said Kenny.

'Aye,' said Harry. 'You know Kenny here is our *cultural* role model. Look at them shoes,' he said, leaning his head across the bar to grimace in the direction of Kenny's slip-ons. 'I have to say, they are a little *garish* for my tastes. Spring's a girl from the streets at night...'

'How's your gin and tonic?' said Alan, to Kenny.

'You want some more tonic?' said Harry.

'Oh just give me a Guinness, for Christ's sake,' said Kenny.

'Good man,' said Harry, to murmurs of approval all around.

'Load of sugar in that tonic anyway,' said Alan.

'So that's your diet gone, eh?' said Harry.

I sipped from my pint and looked around. There was a TV high in the corner, covered in a thick film of dust, and a row of single malts below the optics. Above the optics there were two framed photographs, one of Ian Rankin and another of Ken Stott.

'I smelled the spring on the smoky wind...my wife used to sing that part. Dirty old town, dirty old town...'

'So do you know Mr Rankin then?' I asked.

'Ian, oh aye. Used to come in here when he didn't have a pot to piss in. I hope he comes in soon. I've got stacks of mail for him.'

'People just send it here?'

'Aye. From all over. I'll chop you down, like an old dead tree...'

Alan lumbered off a stool and made his way sighing to the toilet.

'Clouds are drifting, across the moon…'

'You see these tourists, they're good for business here. Good for Harry, so you can't complain too much,' said Kenny. 'Oh, here's the brochure for the book festival.'

'Wonder if Ian's on it,' said Harry.

'I don't know, let me look. Oh aye, there he is.'

'You know I'll have to read something by him now I've come in here. What's the best one to start with?' I asked.

'*Knots and Crosses,*' said Alan, returning from the toilet.

I looked at my watch and got another pint of Best. I listened some more to the voices, the banter, the kind of company I'd missed. The afternoon had seemed to pass slowly compared to the morning. I imagined everyone rushing around outside. Sunlight shone on the optics, giving them an agreeable glow. Necking the last of my pint, I thought briefly of alternatives to the train.

'I'll have to go,' I said.

'Oh, you're going?' said Harry.

'Yep.'

'Good luck with your job. Hope you get it,' said Alan.

'Aye, good luck,' said Kenny, gulping his Guinness.

'Aye, all the best,' said Harry. 'Saw a train set the night on fire…'

'Cheers,' I said, giving them the thumbs up as I walked back out onto the cobbled road.

People in suits commingled in the early evening sunshine. Hundreds waited to cross at the traffic lights near the train station, and on reaching the station rushed through the barriers to their respective platforms. I had a powerful urge to turn around, and so I did.

'You're back then?' said Harry.

'Yep, missed it.'

'You missed the train? Can't you get the next one?'

'No, I got a cheap ticket. It was only valid for that one.'

'Get yourself a pint,' said Kenny. 'I'm sure we'll think of something.'

'Might as well.'

I sat back on the same stool as before, and started on another pint of Best. There was a lull in the conversation. I could hear the gentle rubbing sound as Harry dried pint pots with a tea towel.

'What elevates this pub to master's level?' I asked, finally. 'And how does this pub situate itself in the contemporary field?'

'Eh?' said Harry.

'If this pub...how does this pub elevate itself to master's level?'

'Okay...?' said Alan.

'And how does this pub situate itself in the contemporary field?'

'When you say, "situate itself in the contemporary field",' asked Kenny, 'what do you mean?'

'Near the fucking window,' said Alan.

'No, no, no, Alan, come on, be fair. This is a *serious* question,' said Harry. 'And this is what they asked you in the interview?'

'Yep.'

'And what did you say?'

'No, no, I'm asking you, what you'd say.'

'I'd say get another pint,' said Alan.

'No, no. I can go with this. I'd say that the pub speaks for itself,' said Harry. 'And that my name is above the door. In letters above the door.'

'Fair enough,' I said. 'So then, what elevates this place to master's level?'

'Master's?'

'Yeah.'

'Kenny here has a master's. But look at those *shoes*. Listen, this pub has a PhD, never mind a master's. But we don't need a PhD. Or a master's. If it was me, I would have told them that they were asking the wrong questions.'

'Sounds like bollocks to me,' said Alan.

'Alan, you're interrupting the *intellectual flow* here,' said Harry.

'Okay then, Harry,' I said, 'what questions would *you* have asked?'

'Well, *now* you're asking. Let me just *cogitate* a moment here.'

Houtsiplou
Kate North

Jo is going fifty in a forty but it's okay. She is in the Vale and her previous speeding tickets were in the city. They are different authorities. The rain drives down. It is windy and the moisture on the tarmac is blown towards the gutter in waves.

She pulls in at her designated parking bay ten minutes before the gate closes. Her flight is red on the screen and she just makes it in time. Through security she can tell which travellers will be on her flight. She counts the suits and hopes she gets the smallest one next to her. She sits down by the gate. It feels like it is day and night all at once with the strip lighting and the suspended ceiling looming above. Jo notices a CCTV camera next to the light and smiles at it.

The flight is called to board and she gets in line. The plane is very small. It's so small that one needs to place hand luggage on a trolley for the hold. Jo takes a newspaper from her bag before leaving it on the trolley. She knows that she won't read the paper on the flight.

As the plane quickly fills Jo is happy to be placed next to an empty seat. They take off and Jo unwraps a pear shaped sweet then places it in her mouth. The plane roars and reaches up. It tilts to the

73

coast and Jo can see the white chimney of the power station with
the field of coal next to it. For a while it feels like they are not
moving, that they are suspended above the land like a zeppelin at
the end of a long and invisible rope.

Then they pull above the coast and the land and the
buildings are gone. Light bounces from the wings and the little
flaps shut themselves. There are clouds below and clouds above. Jo
presumes they are not too high because this is short haul. She
declines the offer of a hot drink and asks for water instead. Jo once
spoke with a pilot who said he would never have tea or coffee on a
plane because it is impossible for water to boil at flight altitude. She
imagines low-grade coffee granules gradually dissolving in a flask
of tepid water as she bites into her complimentary cereal bar.

When the land begins to reappear she checks that her
seatbelt is still fastened. The plane noses its way down. Green and
yellow squares emerge along with the odd patch of blue. Roads
become visible and Jo thinks about birds using them to navigate.
Researchers discovered that some birds use arterial roads and
motorways as we use road maps and sat nav. Even if there is a
more direct route the birds still follow the roads.

At ten minutes to land Jo moves her table into the upright
position and looks down to see wind turbines stretched out in
rows. As the plane hangs lower cubes of grey come into view along
with patches of houses, then bigger blocks of buildings, train
tracks, canals. Jo looks at the water. The plane judders and the
flight attendant smiles awkwardly towards the passengers from the
front of the cabin. The plane swings out and then turns inwards

above a large triangular field and it's as though the field is pointing the way. As the plane dips down to the runway the sky becomes more blue than grey.

In the terminal she sits and places her newspaper on her lap. It could be day or night with the strip lighting and the suspended ceiling. She opens the newspaper to page twelve and scans the columns. She sees it handwritten in small block capitals between two columns: *HOUTSIPLOU.*

The restaurant is located on the edge of Place Rouppe just off Rue du Midi. It is not the sort of area you would stumble across as a tourist and it is also away from the bureaucratic trail. In the centre of Place Rouppe there is a large statue on a fountain in the middle of a roundabout. It is a white marble woman holding aloft a laurel wreath with her right hand, about thirty feet tall. There is a train station a few streets away and as Jo watches the door of the restaurant she can hear the sighs of carriages departing. Outside sit three men in their twenties swigging bottles of beer and smoking.

When she enters she scans the room for the best empty table and starts over to it. She is surprised to be stopped by a member of staff who asks for her reservation. It is a kitsch burger and grill bar with cartoon murals on the wall and a student kind of vibe. She is led up to the first floor where she is sat at a table opposite the pass. She watches the chef put out two burgers with salad and one steak frites then she orders a glass of water and a bottle of raspberry beer. As this is a corner building there are two walls with windows.

There is one wall that links to the next building and another wall with a door to the toilets that she presumes leads to a back stairs. Next to that is a door to the kitchen and a dumb waiter with an out of order sign stuck to it. The murals on the wall are brightly coloured and they echo the style of The Beatles' *Yellow Submarine* album with a bit of the cover of *Sgt. Pepper's* thrown in for good measure. On one mural there is a funny little figure of a man with an outsized face. He looks like Jon Bon Jovi and has a speech bubble coming out from mouth that reads 'nous sommes quand-meme tous des Europeens'. Jo translates this with her basic French and wonders if she really understands it.

She watches the main staircase then tells the waiter that she will order her meal when her friend arrives. She flicks through the menu and reads an explanation of the restaurant's weird name. Apparently it's the name of an imaginary place that also exists, whatever that is supposed to mean. According to legend it stems from the phrase 'Écoute s'il pleut', listen if it's raining. Some miller said it to his son once. It makes Jo think about that village back home where it rained for eighty-five days this year. The residents threw a big party when it stopped and the national news turned up to film it.

Jo takes out her phone and pretends to check messages on it. She swills the beer about in her mouth and then gulps some water. She can hear Anna's voice below stating her reservation and she smiles. When they see each other they kiss twice and grasp each other's shoulders briskly. Anna is wearing grey corduroy flares about two sizes too big for her and a long woollen jumper that has a huge neck resting upon her shoulders in folds. She looks like a small insect emerging from its cocoon.

'Funny place,' says Jo when they have ordered.

'Yeah,' says Anna, 'no one comes here.'

'Funny name,' says Jo.

'Thought it would remind you of home,' says Anna.

They spend a good twenty minutes catching up, it's been ages since they've seen each other face to face. A few years back they were meeting regularly but then Anna went to a station out east. Now their paths cross from time to time but it is mainly virtual.

When their food comes Anna gets about two bites in and then places a folded piece of paper on the table under Jo's napkin.

'It's eyes only,' says Anna.

Jo nods and keeps on eating. She dips her fries in ketchup and mayo then posts them into her mouth, one after another. After a few beats of silence she stops and slips the paper from under her napkin up her sleeve.

'Remember when I left the Ukraine desk?' says Anna, who then picks up her burger and takes a bite.

Jo nods. Anna picks a fry up and pokes it around her plate.

'Ludo was ill again and I took a few months off?' Jo remembers her brother coming out of remission and going back on chemo, Anna had been in a bad way.

'I offered to go to Syria straight after his funeral.'

Jo doesn't know what to say so she just keeps nodding and eating.

Anna tells her that in the end Ludo's death was a kind of relief. After it she didn't fear anything, she was happy to volunteer.

'Uh-huh,' says Jo.

Then Anna tells her about a family she helped escort out of Damascus. A husband and wife with two children. A boy and a girl. The boy was six and the girl was eight. The father was initially pro Assad, ISIL wanted him because he was a coder. He was willing to cooperate with the coalition for safe passage, what he was giving up was useful for the FSA. The family would be taken into Lebanon and from there they would make their way to the UK via Greece. Anna spent an afternoon with them. She was talking the father through their new documents when there was a bombing raid. They went to shelter and the kids were crying. At this point Anna starts to tear up. She takes a sip of her drink and continues.

'They reminded me of Ludo and me when we were younger. She was a tomboy and he was really softly spoken. When he started to cry she held him close to her and sang to him until he settled. She was called Rima and he was called Sami,' says Anna using the neck of her jumper to wipe tears from her face. She is sniffing quietly and Jo wants to hold her hand but knows better.

'Two weeks later they were killed in an explosion at a bakery. The whole family. They had got as far as Beirut. I saw a picture of the kids. They were lying face down in a pile of rubble next to each other. Half of Sami's skull was missing and all of Rima's clothes were torn from her, except for her shoes and socks. They were both grey with dust from the concrete. The blood coming from Sami's skull was mixed with dust too, it was really dark. The picture looked black and white even though it was colour. It could have been from another time entirely, not just two weeks after having met them,' says Anna. Then she looks down at her plate and takes a deep breath. She pulls at the necklace around her neck, places her thumb under a pendant and tilts it towards Jo.

'I wanted to show you this.'

'Right,' says Jo.

'It opens up,' says Anna giving it a little shake.

Jo frowns but doesn't say anything. Anna looks directly at Jo.

'But you're back now.'

'Yeah.'

'So things will be calmer,' says Jo smiling.

'Yeah.'

Walking back to her hotel Jo decides that she will have to call it in. Poor Anna. She obviously needs to get out. Even if only for a while. It happens to more people than the service would like to acknowledge. It's nothing to be ashamed of. Jo reasons that it could happen to her one day. The hotel is not far away, a five-minute walk in the direction of the Grand Place. It's called the rather un-exotic Hotel Bedford. It is one of those old hotels that was clearly glamorous when it first opened. The reception is large with marble floors and pillars. There is dark wood panelling on the walls and emerald green rugs throughout. A sweeping staircase to the left of the reception desk leads to a mezzanine where you can look down on everyone coming and going. The decor in the restaurant, bar and bedrooms is shabby 1970s and you can only get

Freeview channels on the TVs. The Wi-Fi connection is variable and Jo is not looking forward to the rest of the evening so she stops off en route and picks up some beers.

In her room she tries to move the bed back so that she has enough space to do some stretches but can't manage it. She has stayed at the Bedford before but this is the smallest room yet. She takes a sock off and, standing on a chair, places it over the smoke detector outside the bathroom. She goes into the bathroom and shuts the door behind her. She unfolds the message Anna gave her over the sink, reads it then sets light to it with a cigarette lighter. She washes the ash away and sits on the loo while the bathroom fan whirrs. After a minute she returns to the bedroom, puts the TV on a news channel and sets it to mute. She checks in with the office on her mobile and confirms she will go for a debrief when she returns.

After she is most of the way through a beer she receives a text message from an unknown number. It reads, *sooner rather than later*. She gets up, puts her phone in her jeans' pocket and her jacket on. She makes sure she has got her key then heads down to reception and sits on a chair by one of the panelled walls for a couple of minutes. She pretends to check her phone. She is certain that she was not followed. She heads outside and speed walks to the Grand Place. Even though it is getting late it is as busy as always. She goes into a chocolate shop and takes her time looking up and down the shelves. She puts a couple of boxes into a shopping basket then pretends to listen to a voicemail on her phone. When she is certain she is okay she buys the souvenir boxes of truffles and steps out into the evening bustle. The Grand Place is a huge square surrounded by 18th-century buildings built in Baroque, Gothic and Louis XIV styles. The buildings are lit up at night and they look like ghosts rising from the ground, flares of light catching arches and towers. Crowds of tourists mill around so that it is impossible to stand still for any length of time. Everyone looks up to the buildings, phones flashing as images of the square are captured over and over throughout the night, every night. Jo bobs through the crowd and considers going for a drink at a bar before deciding to head back to the Bedford.

On her bed she sips a beer and opens one of the boxes of truffles. She re-reads the text message and presumes it is from Anna who is clearly having a major wobble. She pops another truffle into her mouth. They are brilliant. People can say what they like about Belgium, but they do excellent chocolate and beer. Jo feels she could live here happily. The flat grey of the place wouldn't bother her at all, as long as she had a ready supply of beer and chocolate. The TV is still on from before. That's how crappy the hotel is. They are still using keys, no swipe cards that activate the electricity in the room. The key has a huge fob shaped like a truncheon. You could easily knock someone out with it. Jo places her key under her pillow and reaches for another chocolate. As she does so she looks up to the TV. The news is reporting live from a district on the other side of the city. Jo turns the sound up. There has been an explosion. There are flames coming from several buildings and the camera crew is filming firefighters as they tackle the blaze. It looks big. It's in the Molenbeek district which isn't too far from the Bedford, about fifteen minutes' walk or half that via the metro. Then she hears the distant screech of sirens headed to the fire.

Jo's phone vibrates. Another text from the same number as before. This time it's an address. She doesn't recognise it but when she looks it up her ears thud and her mouth goes dry. It's in Molenbeek.

Outside it is raining. She pulls her jacket collar up around her ears and sticks close to buildings as she speed walks. The sound of sirens grows and she can see that the metro station is blocked off with armed guards and police with dogs as she heads past it. She is wearing canvas trainers that are totally sodden and she can feel the water funnelling from the back of her head straight down her neck. The nearer she gets to the address the more and more vehicles with sirens she sees charging past. Police, fire, ambulance, riot vans, then two bomb disposal units and some army jeeps. She can hear a helicopter as she ducks down an alleyway and looks at the map on her phone. She thinks the address is an adjacent block to the one the explosion was in. She will have to go back on herself and take a wide loop around to come at the address from a different angle or else she will get stopped.

Jo stands looking at Anna who is kneeling on the floor with her head face down on the sofa. There is a hole in the back of her neck and blood has spread across the upholstery, which has acted like a wick. It's a clean kill. From the lounge window Jo can see that the fire is still raging and heading in this direction. She hears another explosion and decides to hurry up. She takes a picture of Anna on her phone. Then she kneels behind her and takes the locket from around her neck. She puts it in her back pocket then thinks better of it and places it in her bra. The metal is still warm. She takes the stairs all the way down to basement car park and leaves through the back entrance.

Jo decides that she should not use her booked flight to return. She gets a ticket for the train and even though she arrives in plenty of time she only just makes it. The increased security is immense and everyone is being searched thoroughly before the gates. On top of this there are refugees from the camp burning tyres on the track outside the tunnel again. Several trains have been cancelled and this one is packed. Jo has an aisle seat next to a teenager who looks bored. She has large pink headphones that match her long stripy pink socks. She is wearing a black miniskirt and David Bowie T-shirt. She sits curled up on her seat facing the window for the whole journey. When the train stops at Lille more people get on. Some have to stand in the aisles, which never happens on this route. When they are through the tunnel Jo checks the news on her phone. The flames in Molenbeek are now dying due to the heavy rain. The Premier has announced a state of emergency in the capital. Jo picks at a piece of fluff on the arm of the brown seat. It reminds her of a sofa in her parents' house growing up. It also reminds her of the Hotel Bedford.

When she arrives in St Pancras she makes her way to Paddington. She walks out of the station and heads to a pub a couple of streets away. It is full of commuters killing time before their trains. Outside people with luggage huddle beneath canopies chain smoking and warming themselves under heat lamps. Jo gets a pint and heads to the back of the pub. She takes her paper out and places it on the table in front of her. Beneath the table she holds Anna's necklace in her hand. She opens the locket and sees a small memory card. She takes her laptop out of her bag and inserts the memory card into it. It has one file on it, which she opens. It's a picture of a rowan tree on the edge of some scrubland. Jo recognises it immediately.

When she gets there it is muddy as hell. It takes her nearly an hour to dig down to the metal box. The rain has turned the ground to mush making it difficult to deal with. The box is about double the width of a shoebox and although it is not terribly heavy it is awkward. Jo has to drag it back to her car. She knocks the lock from the box. She makes a quick check of the contents and then checks her surroundings for onlookers. No one. She starts the car anyway and drives to a place she has been with no one else. A track near a viaduct at the back of a housing estate.

She flicks through the images in front of her. There must be a hundred of them. Most of them are photographs but a handful are pictures clipped from newspapers. Mainly children though as she gets to the back of the pile more adults emerge. Their bodies lie across rubble or in forest clearings. Some are in cars, slumped forwards or back against their seats. A number are in bed. One, a picture of a woman with her child, echoes Anna's final resting pose. The two corpses are slumped forward onto a sofa next to each other holding hands. They both have entry holes in the back of their necks. On the reverse of the pictures Jo recognises Anna's neat handwriting. Little block capitals spelling out the acronyms of different agencies and organisations. Then next to each acronym there is a place name and a date:

NDS, Kabul, 12/01/13
JIO, Homs, 09/05/14
IDF, Jabalia, 07/03/12

The picture of Rima and Sami is just as Anna described. It could be from WWII. Jo has to look hard to see the traces of twenty-first-century colour beneath the rubble and the dust. The back of the picture reads:

SIS, Beirut, 10/10/15

Jo wonders what on earth Anna thought she would do with all of this. Set up a bloody museum? Jesus. Among the pictures are also a number of passports and travel cards, along with a range of foreign currency. Jo thinks back to Anna in her lounge and remembers that she has the image stored on her phone. She knows that she will have to haul the box and its contents with her back to the office. Fuck. And she will have to write it all up, tonight. She shuts the box and gets into the front of her car.

The rain has let up a little and light drops patter across the windscreen. Jo only needs her wipers on the first setting. The rain sounds like someone drumming their fingers softly against a coffee table. She feels for the picture of Sami and Rima that she has placed in her jacket pocket. After ten minutes on the road she listens for the rain and it has stopped. She turns her wipers off and looks up to the sky. She thinks it will certainly pour down again before she gets back.

The Two Parties
Gary Raymond

An unseasonal mist hung at eye-level.
'Black cabs are everywhere now,' you said,
Staring vapidly at the one before us at the traffic lights.
'Not just London, and I'm not
Sure how I feel about that.
One of the many corruptions of Globalisation.'
With a curve of the neck, a roll of the eyes.
'Do you think if the country votes Leave
Tonight, the Black Cabs will be called
Back to being a thing of London?
Do you think that's what they want, the Leavers?'
'I doubt it,' you said, 'but the metaphor
                        is a powerful one.'
Those eyes again, sarcastic this time.

'Do you think the French will want
                        their baguettes back?' I said.
Such innocent times.

The door opened like a grin.

The voices and golden light within
Made it difficult to keep the ideas
Of time and place close to mind;
Everything was of a swirl,
Time back, time front, time as tool.

Timid, was the word you used,
Under your breath as you perused
The other guests and the layout of the place.
We walked through the hallway into the light,
You slinked your cardigan off your shoulders.
At the last party, the Scottish Referendum party,
They handed out badges, they asked
You on the door: are you for Liberty
Or Servitude? But that wasn't
This party; that was two streets down.
That night's host was here too,
Another academic in the village of the damned,
Still smarting, hoping for a UKIP
Army to deliver him an ugly reprisal.
You cocked your wine glass at him,
And he dipped his head back.
So many curious gestures;
A study in itself.

'I like his jacket,' I said; 'I've been
Looking for a corduroy jacket. In Brown.'

'I don't believe that is at the forefront
Of your mind,' you said. 'You're right,' I said.
'I'm nervous and when I'm nervous I talk about
                  other people's jackets.
Tell me about the badges.'

'Even then it was a strange theatre,
Splitting us up the way they did. YES
And NO. The efforts of a corduroy
Academic to stir debate, like a parlour
Game, like throwing car keys into a fruit bowl
And matching up the salivators.'
'What if you didn't care and only
Turned up for the wine?'
'It was heavily encouraged you take a side.
The funny thing was the YES badges
Were undersized, unreadable, malformed
Mockeries of the message they conveyed.
Feeble was the word and the word was YES.'
'Do you think it had an influence on
the result?' 'It couldn't have helped,' you said.

The food – the spread – was multicultural.
Small 'm', small 'c';
Pastry-wrapped insurgents of exotic rarities
Purchased by the armful from a high end highstreet
Supermarket, the waft of light panic and cardboard

Coming down from the world foods aisle.
'Is the wine a selection from around the continent?' I said.
'The continent as it still stands now, tonight, before
The votes are counted. European for the Remainers – a confident
Range of sweet German, effusive Bulgarian and nutty Italian?
And wine from the peat bogs of Norfolk for the Leavers?'
'I don't think there are many of *that sort* here,' you said,
An air of disappointment to your voice; your lust for balance
tempered
By your generosity of wit. You moved toward
A group huddled at a table in the corner, as I considered
What I had just said. Are there even peat bogs in Norfolk?
Am I qualified to vote on matters of our European future
When I know so little about my own country?

'Badges would have been good here,' I caught up to you.
'Leave spiralled into the rings of a spitfire wing, Remain
Tattooed onto the outstretched arm of an SS uniform.'
There is a delicate balance to getting the message right.

There were complaints in the Scottish Referendum
That the Independence movement had the upper hand.
They had commandeered the word *Yes*,
The word that brought John and Yoko together,
The word that split up The Beatles.
You don't get much more British than The Beatles.
For the Independence movement in the end

It didn't work, the positive campaign fizzled
And swamped and Scotland stayed tethered.
We will wait and see if what the Unified Kingdom does next
Will be as culturally significant as what the Beatles
Might have done had they stayed as one.

'How do you think the Beatles would have reacted to punk?'
I said to a grey-eyed professor with an Iris Murdoch haircut.
'It is quite impossible to suppose such things,' Iris said.
'There are so many variables. What influences
Would have turned them on in the five years
Between their breakup and the birth of punk,
Or wherever you decide to put that on your counterfactual
timeline?
Are you sure punk would have even happened?
Are you sure The Beatles would not have collapsed
All musical form as we know it? Brought Stockhausen
Into the mainstream, like they almost did with the modal music of
India?'
She looked up at me with the concrete of purpose.
'I think they would have ridden the wave,' I said.
She left, the professor, excusing herself for the pull of the spread,
And my attempts at stirring revolution in the room stayed flat.

No wine here older than three years. But vintage
Is largely a myth, a marketing term for misremembered youth.
Trust you to have found the strangest corner,

The surrealist secret in the Dadaist diorama.
A conversation in German, French, and Welsh,
Conspiratorial and sublime, probably avoiding all clichés.
It seemed an inconvenience for them
To revert to English for you, and I often
Think of this ragtail roundtable of non-binary academics
Now, after the vote, that foreign languages
Are forbidden on public transport. They huddled
Then, by the sliding doors, and they huddle now
By candlelight somewhere, iron in the soul, awaiting
The great purge of intellectuals and the firing squads
In the snow. 'Remember those modern language
Professors at the Referendum party,' you will say,
And I will say that I do. 'None of them have been
Seen since Tuesday.' And I will *not* say
Because it will *not* be appropriate, given the rumours
Of death squads, 'Has anybody checked to see
If they're huddled by the sliding doors?'

But I will *want* to say that, because
The Brexiters may rob me of my hope,
And they may deprive me of my humanity,
Make woodchippings of my resolve,
But they will *not* take my sense of humour.

There used to be a time when folk would gather
Round the wireless for occasions such as this.

A monarch's address, coronation, abdication,
A prime minister's suicide note, the odd jubilee.
The flat screen was on the wall, above
The mantelpiece, hung like a portrait, I switched
My weight from foot to foot, the chairs
Taken up by an eminence of professors. One of them
Examined the TV at close quarters with characteristic
Inquiry, bending his neck in curiosity to see the bracket,
As if searching for a hidden safe – the drawing
Room intrigue would not end there. Another,
With a pleased look, said, 'It appears
The writing is going to be on the wall.'
You were the only one in the room not to laugh.
We talked about having t-shirts made: *Flat Screens are for
Scroungers.*
You see, it was a mood of relaxed optimism,
Of a future bounding with good, the future
Like a Labrador puppy unravelling a toilet roll.
We had congregated to celebrate our souls,
To celebrate our inevitable modern mature defeat of stupidity,
To celebrate love, culture, truth, liberalism.
And then Sunderland fell.

The corduroy Scot stood to your shoulder
And breathed wheezily into his highball of stout.
'This will get colourful from here on in,' he said.
Essays were birthed with whispers, a few declared

With thunder and the pop of dawning grief.
The party was over before it began.

There was nothing left to say, other than that
The rivers run into the sea,
That *hevel* would be the theme of the summer.

You dropped me at the corner of the park;
I felt a walk some way would bear meaning,
At least as gesture if not as carrier
Of some Damascan fruit. The last
I saw of you, a Dutch portrait in the window
Of the driver's side, you quoted Shakespeare
At me, which was out of character in that it was consoling
As well as four hundred years outside
Your academic field. I took this as a sign
The rules had changed that night with immediate effect.

> *If there be nothing new, but that which is,*
> *Hath been before, how are our brains beguiled,*
> *Which labouring for invention, bear amiss,*
> *The second burden of a former child.*

'The new world is the old world,' you said,
Helping me along. As you drove off
Into the night, I thought of the Dadaists again,
That they knew all those years ago,
In the golden years of European fascism,
That a society is most clearly defined by what

It throws away. It will be a summer of meaninglessness,
A year of meaninglessness,
And as I walked through the park,
And the sound of your car rippled into the night,
I knew that nobody would ever get what they want,
And every single thing that happens in the world
Will be fully loaded with meaninglessness.

You're all Playing It Wrong
Anne Griffin

Nine and a half years ago Lorna arrived at my apartment door.

'I have wonderful news, Angie. I'm having a baby.'

She had no idea who the father was. Someone she'd met in Saint Pat's, she thought. She was thirty-two and beautiful. I mean really spectacularly beautiful. Tall, full lipped with long golden hair. I, on the other hand, had hair that clumped rather than bounced, fattened rather than flowed and legs that refused to stretch beyond the height of the kitchen table.

My mother turned into an old woman overnight when I passed on the news of the pregnancy. My father held his head in his hands and said:

'Well, she's done it now.'

I glanced at a muted Brian Dobson on the RTE evening news and asked who wanted tea.

I knew from an early age that Lorna was different from the other big sisters on our road. They hung out together in relative harmony, playing games in which they bossed us smaller ones about. That was until Lorna arrived.

'You're all playing it wrong.' 'No, I won't give it back.' 'It's mine,' she'd whine.

My toes curled when I heard her. I soon became adept at slipping out of the house without her noticing. And yet, her first serious episode didn't come until years later.

'It was so freeing throwing it all away,' she told us, when Dad brought her and her ten refuse sacks home from college in Galway. He'd found her pacing the student accommodation, raving about voices and demons. Her flatmates had picked up everything she'd thrown out of her bedroom window: books, clothes, the lot. They kept vigil until he arrived; their front door locked in case she made a run for it.

That was her first time in Pat's, from then on she became a regular in hospital. Every year or so, falling in love with whichever psychiatrist she was assigned; man or woman, it never bothered her. And when after two months, or three, or, once it went so far as six, she came out again to face the strain of the 'normal' world, my parents insisted she lead an independent life. Every penny they had went into creating a world in which she survived and sometimes thrived. A ground-floor apartment, five minutes' walk from them, a job whenever she felt like it in my father's coffee shop and as much therapy as everyone involved could endure. I, on the other hand, chose the city and quantity surveying.

After Tippy was born, we set up rotas to help. Mornings for Mam, afternoons for Dad and evenings for me. For a while it worked. But slowly things slipped. We'd arrive to find Tippy in nappies hanging between her legs like cow udders fit to burst – the place in disarray. Then, one evening I had to work late. Lorna, faced with a distraught Tippy, decided a drive might calm her. Not owning a car, let alone a license, she had snatched the keys from my parents' hallway. Slipped in without them even noticing. When she rounded a bend near Newcastle in Wicklow she simply kept turning the steering wheel 'right into the starry night', she said.

She was found wandering the road. A woman driving in the opposite direction passed her and then stopped a mile or so on when she saw the car in a field, lights on and doors open. It was she who called the police. After, when the social worker had left my parents' house, Lorna begged me to take Tippy. Held on to my hand and squeezed it tight on the brown-flowered couch in Mam's front room. Lines of clear snot running down her face, mingling with her tears.

'Please, Angie,' she had cried, 'just for a while.'

*

Tippy was a year and half when I fostered her. She slipped into my world like she was always meant to be there with her butterfly kisses and white wispy hair and 'round and round the garden's. And her toys, carted around wherever we went in her Dora the Explorer bag. Between the ages of two and four she was all about Terence, the one-toothed soft green crocodile, who tragically we mislaid on a holiday in Spain. I knew, far away Terence sat forlorn at the departure gate in Malaga as I rocked Tippy's heartbreak like she was a newborn; her little blue diamond eyes nodding off only to open in shock two seconds later with the realisation that he was missing all over again. We 'found' Terence seven days and one credit card bill later, when, faced with an eternity of shattered sleep, I bought an identical imposter.

'Terwence,' Tippy squealed, in heart-stopping joy that Friday when I picked her up from crèche and she found him waiting in her car seat.

Then came the Lego Friends phase. Worried by the abundance of those skinny girls in miniskirts, I blew off the dust from the USA biscuit tin that held my old Lego, long abandoned in my mother's attic. Soon, red, blue and green blocks began to mingle in that pink and purple world. Happily, those Lego women left their horses and hairdryers behind to become engineers and pilots, building and flying the world.

'But you know, Mom,' Tippy said, after we'd completed the Burj Khalifa, 'I still want to be a pop star.'

From age eight it's all been about screens. Those Lego ladies look on sadly now as Tippy hangs out with Creepers and Endermen. It's embarrassing to admit that I've tried and failed to enforce the 'only at weekends' rule.

'But, only a half-hour, okay?' I say, defeated. But she's already lost to me online.

She's always known Lorna is her birth mom.

'Is Mammy Lorna, sad mammy or happy mammy today?' she asked me when she was four years old and kneeling up on the armchair in our sitting room, watching for Lorna to arrive. We never discovered the answer to the question as she never showed.

'That's okay, Mom,' Tippy said, looking at my worried expression, stroking my face, as I hunkered down in front of her in an attempt at consolation.

Other days, Lorna arrived unannounced or late at night, expecting to find Tippy still awake. Or sometimes she'd phone my mobile at 11 a.m. on a weekday wanting to speak to her.

'It's a school day, Lor,' I'd say.

'School, of course. She does that now. I'll call her later.' But she usually forgot.

Tippy doesn't talk much about Lorna. Mainly that's my job. But every so often she'll ask me what my favourite thing about her is.

'Her hair. No wait, her laugh,' I said once.

'I like her shoes,' she replied.

Tippy's nine now. Tall and stunning as I knew she would be. Smiley but sometimes sad. But who isn't? What I mean is, she's a normal kid.

Last week Lorna phoned the school. They've grown used to her erratic inquiries on Tippy's progress. They tell her, as do I, that Tippy's doing great. But after, when the principal called to update me, she said:

'That's three times in the last month, Angie. I'm wondering is there something we should know, for Tippy's sake.'

'Nothing,' I said.
But in truth I hadn't heard from Lorna in ten months.

Lorna summoned me four days ago. And now I'm sitting at the
Fallon and Byrne window, a half empty cup of Earl Grey tea in
front on me, wearing my ten-year-old jeans and Penny's best
hoodie while at the counter she dons tailored clothes and short-
cropped hair, Ellen Degeneres kind of short. Confident, I think. The
thought delays me in responding to her pointing at my cup. I shake
my head and she concludes her order with a brush of her hand that
teeters between sweet and rude. I can't decide.

'Look at you stranger. What's been going on?' I say, as she
takes the stool beside me.

'Everything, Angela, everything.'

She smiles and pushes an invisible strand of hair behind her
ear.

'Sounds intriguing. Too distracting to make a phone call or
to pop by?'

'I left messages.'

'Yes, I got all two of them. Mam and Dad were worried you
know, not to mention Tippy.'

'I told them I was fine,' she said, her smile beginning to fade.

We allow the hustle of the city street to distract us.

'You look good,' I say, after a moment.

'I feel good. Really good.'

'So, go on, tell me all.'

She pauses just for a second, like she's considering if I'm trustworthy enough.

'I've met someone.'

'You're not pregnant?'

'Christ, Angela.' She huffs at the window and the passing shoppers.

'Sorry. I'm sorry… tell me?'

'This time everything's different.' She becomes shy, in a way that is unnerving. I brace myself. 'He has healed me.' Her face turns fully to me now and her eyes hold mine.

Fuck.

'A psychiatrist, then?'

'Better. An actualist.'

Double fuck.

'A whatist?'

'Someone who's made me see the hard truth of who I am. Seb. He's based in London. And well… he's just wonderful. I'm back, Angie, I'm back, I truly am.'

'Back?'

'My journey, is over. I have returned to myself.'

My toes curl as I sip my by-now cold Earl Grey.

'I want her back now, Angela. It's time,' she says, just like that, like it's time to catch the train. My brain juggles her words around in my head for a bit until they finally find an order and I begin to understand their awfulness, their inconceivable awfulness.

'I want you to know I am grateful for all you've done. Seb and I have met with a solicitor and have begun the procedure to end the fostering process.'

I cannot speak. My silence sits unhappily between us, not knowing where to look.

I lay my hands against the counter edge and wonder if I'm about to rise. But I simply press against the varnished wood until my fingers begin to tap at its smoothness. I watch them, envying their determined thud. And then I close my eyes and breathe in the coffee-filled air. I feel its freshness hit the back of my throat. I hold it there for as long as I dare before slowly letting it escape back to where it came from, through my tight-lipped mouth.

'I'm moving to London. Seb can get Tippy into a very good school in St John's Wood. He has connections.'

'What?' I say, opening my eyes.

'We think it's for the best. A fresh start for everyone. You can get your life back.'

'My life? But Lorna… she *is* my life.'

She says nothing but raises her coffee to her heart-shaped mouth.

'She's not a cat that I've been babysitting for the weekend, you know. You can't just take her. Eight years, Lorna, eight.'

'Seb and I are well aware of all of that. We are committed to this.'

'He's never even met her. How can he be committed to someone he doesn't even know?'

'He's committed to me.'

'Well, someone needs committing that's for sure.'

'That's not fair, Angela. We can work this out.'

'Jesus, Lorna. She's a child.'

'My child, Angela. Mine.'

It is then my fist bangs against the counter, startling the cutlery into clanging against the crockery.

'You really think I'll let some New-Aged flake called Seb take my daughter. Cop on Lorna. Cop the hell on.' My words trail after me as I elbow my way through the gawping tables, past the aproned waitress who takes a step backwards like I'm diseased.

Outside, I shake. My palm splays against the granite column, desperate for its support. My body doubles and I heave. When nothing rises I gulp at the air, pulling it in until it quietens my lurching stomach and racing heart. And then I push away into the path of determined shoppers. I pass my sister still seated in the window. She does not see me now. Her head is bent, her hands gripping her forehead and it stops me. I know that harried look so well. A look I've rescued far too many times. And for a second, I think of knocking on the glass, to reach her with my smile that will surely make everything okay. But it is fleeting. Instead, my legs turn me into the throng and transport me home to my daughter, to my Tippy.

Joe
Jeanette Sheppard

We'd spend hours playing on the rocks by the river before they found Joe down there. Ali used to grab our hands – mine and Joe's – and we'd run through the farm out to the fields.

The only place she ran after they found Joe was to her room, until she was old enough to run away for good. She only came back to see me every January, on my birthday: she said it was her *duty* to see her little sister. She never unzipped her coat; never brought a present or a card. I always got the fire going in the kitchen but that zip never budged. It being my fiftieth this year didn't change a thing. She sat, as she always did, when she visited, in Dad's worn old armchair near the back door of the kitchen, perched on the edge, ready for the off, like when she was a kid.

'Happy fiftieth,' she mumbled, as she sat in Dad's chair and jabbed at the stuffing that was seeping out; every year, just before she arrived, I'd pull it back out again: she needed something to do while we were sitting saying nothing. I was thinking about something to say when she started to shake and mutter – I couldn't make it out. She tried to get out of the chair but her hands slipped on the worn arms and she was left with clumps of stuffing in her hands. She wanted to shuffle forward but her muscles wouldn't allow it. I rang for an ambulance.

Two fellas turned up and carried her upstairs to her old room at the back. They checked her out. When they came back down they said she had a bladder infection; said they'd get the doctor and he'd make out a prescription for some antibiotics; said it was probably best if she stayed here for a couple of days – is that alright? Not ideal, I said. I see, they said. I told them I'd keep my eye on her – you have to look after family. The young one with the bitten nails had another chew while his mate sat in Dad's chair and filled out his forms.

After they'd gone I went upstairs. Ali was asleep. They'd taken her coat off, thrown a sheet on the bed and another on top of her; I'd told them they'd find some in the airing cupboard. They'd opened the windows. They'd said she needed to cool down – it was her temperature that was making her shake. I thought I'd better fix something up at the window. Not that there was anyone to gawp, only field after field. And the river. I had to do right by my sister though, so I hung her old bedspread from the airing cupboard over the curtain wire that was still across the window.

After the doctor, I kept going up to check on her. Come five-ish I thought I'd better take her some soup and check her temperature. Although we'd held hands as kids we didn't even stand near each other any more. It needed doing though, her temperature. Her fringe was gappy; I didn't realise she had all those lines on her forehead. She looked like that Irish journalist on the news. She probably knew him, probably drank with him in the bar. I managed to touch her head without waking her. She wasn't hot, so I shut the window.

When I went to bed I left the landing light on for her. As a kid, after Joe, she'd always wanted her light left on, even though she was ten. Every night the last thing I saw before I went to sleep was that line of light under my door.

Next morning, when I came in from the cows, she was in Dad's chair, ready for the off. She didn't lift her head, made out she was texting. She looked whiter than the milk.

'You're not right to drive,' I said and pulled off my wellies.

She carried on with her phone. 'Where's all my things from my room, Sam?'

'In the loft.' I walked across the kitchen. The cold pushed through the hole in my sock.

'When did you put them up there?'

'After Mum and Dad died.' I pulled open the dresser drawer to look for the invoice that needed paying.

'Doesn't matter, just wondered. Thanks for looking after me.'

'They said you should stay here for a few days.' I put the mess of papers from the drawer on to the table.

'What are you going to do, Sam – take my keys?' She picked them up from her lap and jangled them. Her Swiss army knife clanked. She started texting again in her other hand.

'Up to you. Probably best if you stay – that's what the paramedics said.'

She stood up to go but collapsed like one of the newborns. She looked up at me from under her fringe.

'Bet you're cold down there,' I said. She lifted her head and showed a bit of her lopsided grin. I bent low, lifted her arm around my shoulder. She turned her head away but I still smelt the wine. I heaved her up; her legs buckled again and she fell back down.

'You've got a sweat on, Sam. Come on, I'm a lot lighter than one of your calves.'

I put her arm back around me and this time she didn't turn her head away. I gave another heave. She was up. We stood for a moment while she got her balance – her arm around my shoulder, my arm around her waist. I inched her towards the chair and held her steady, at arms' length, before she tried to bend and sit.

'You're still sweaty,' she grinned, trying to keep her head upright. I eased her down onto the seat. I went to wipe my forehead but stopped myself. I wasn't going to give her room to remark. I put her feet on the stool and went to fetch a glass of water.

I held out the antibiotic between my thumb and finger. She looked at me like she was ten again, in charge of me and Joe. Her lips went flat. I put the tablet on her palm; she tried to pinch her finger and thumb around it but she couldn't. She looked up at the brown damp patch on the ceiling and opened her mouth. I put the tablet on her wine-stained tongue. She looked down and glared at me, under her heavy eyelids, daring me to have a go. I didn't. I put the glass of water to her lips; she sipped, jerked her head right back and closed her eyes. As she swallowed, the veins in her throat swelled. She handed me the glass and rested her head against the back of Dad's chair. It wasn't long before she drifted off. I went out to meet the fella with the cow feed.

We spent a couple of days talking only about what she wanted to eat. She refused to go anywhere near a bed during daylight and slept in Dad's chair. The first time she was able to walk properly was when the estate agent arrived.

As I came across the yard from the sheds I clocked her through the front window. I unlatched the door to show the estate agent in and saw her hurry back to Dad's chair. I introduced them and he went off to do his measuring.

'Are you selling the farm?' she asked as soon as he'd gone upstairs.

'You certainly earned that award for newspaper writing.'

'You didn't tell me you were selling.'

'Did I have to?'

'You didn't *have* to —' She stopped because the estate agent was leaning his head around the door from the hallway.

'Could I just ask you about the loft, Ms Anderson?'

'It's not necessary to go up there. My sister's not selling.'

The estate agent gave his professional smile. Ali gave hers back. I said I'd get the loft key. Ali stood up. 'There are personal items up there.'

I nodded and told him it was probably best if he left it a few days, until Ali could take what she wanted from the loft.

When I came back in from seeing him off Ali was wearing her old school duffel coat. She'd obviously been in the loft earlier. She hadn't changed shape much since she was a teenager; she was probably even thinner than she used to be. She said, 'My coat isn't warm enough for the walk.'

'The walk?' I said.

'I'll need one of your scarves,' she said as she did up the last duffel toggle, 'and I'll get my gloves from the car on the way.' She walked past me and unlatched the door. 'Hurry up, Sam. We need to get going – it's starting to snow.'

I bent against the cold; Ali stayed ahead of me. Neither of us had been in the fields since they found Joe but we still knew the way. At the wooden gate Ali stopped: this was where, as kids, we'd hear the rush of the river. There was no rush today.

We walked across the next field with Ali still ahead and never looking behind. She slowed as she reached the edge of the field before the river. She turned around to look for me. I caught her up and we stepped through the gap in the hawthorn hedge. From here we could see the two oak trees, by the rocks, one each side of the river. As children we would swing on our rope from oak to oak. Ali, being ten and the eldest, was always referee and judge. There was no contest though: Joe was the best. He was nine, and a year older than me, but slighter. He was so quick sometimes it was like the rope wasn't there. Just him against the sky.

Ali took my arm and we walked from the hawthorn hedge to the river bank. We looked down at the snow landing on the grey frozen water.

We'd stayed later than we should the day Joe fell in the river. It was the end of summer and we were due back at school the next day. Ali had undone the rope, ready for us to go home. Joe wanted to carry on. Ali said it was getting dark: Mum had called four times now. Ali always gave in to Joe though: my place was second in line. I knew that even then. Ali climbed the tree, hooked the rope around the branch and retied the knot. Joe climbed.

The branch was rotten. Just an accident everyone said: the branch was rotten. Joe had fallen; hit his head on the rocks and slipped down the bank into the river. Just an accident. But I knew it wasn't, Ali knew it wasn't: we had both seen the rope slip from the branch. It had been too dark: she hadn't tied the knot properly. The branch had snapped after Joe had fallen.

The rush of the river carried him downstream. Blood moved with him. Ali ran but she couldn't catch up. I sprinted home for help. When they found Joe's body after dark on the mud bank he was still clutching onto the rope.

Now, as the snow began to bury the frozen river Ali moved nearer the bank. She crouched underneath the oak tree and rested her hands either side of a football sized rock. She looked up at me;

snow dripped from her fringe. 'Help steady me, then – you've had enough practice the last few days.'

I stood behind and wrapped my arms tight around her middle. I felt the press of the hip flask in her duffel pocket. I anchored her as she pushed the rock over the edge onto the ice. The thud and crack made us jolt. We leant our heads together.

Three Poems
Rhian Elizabeth

the neurologist

i have lesions,
he says-
multiple.
a disease that attacks my brain
and hacks away at my spinal cord
like a lumberjack.
that's okay
i tell him-
i'm fine with that.
brave or just relieved.
i was worried about your machine-
that in that white tunnel that click clicks
like a typewriter and
bangs like a drum
you'd scanned my brain and saw things
no neurologist should see.
those lesions caused by love,
internet porn

and secrets.
by childhood memories
and brand new scars that
the steroids you just prescribed me
won't ever heal.

junaluska

my online dating profile said i was a catch
which was true
if you happened to find at the end of your rod
a tin can
all folded up
sunk for years at the bottom of that lake.

if it's only at night

i am the moon and
you are the earth.
i stare at you constantly
384 thousand kilometres away
hanging there in space motionless
like a broken disco ball.
you are big
and i am small
but i am grateful to light up your sky
if it's only at night.
the sun takes up most of your time
my yellow nemesis
but i know you look at me too
if it's only at night.
i am always there
and i have to share you with the northern lights
which i admit are more magnificent than me
and with the stars in their millions
that people wish upon
that now and again shoot
just to show off.
no one ever wished upon a moon
but i don't mind
because if it's only at night
you are mine.

That Face, Like a Harvest Moon
Susmita Bhattacharya

Manju sat at the head of the table, cup of strong tea in her hand, and watched her daughter and son-in-law prepare breakfast. They stood shoulder to shoulder, one cooking eggs, the other pouring coffee. She absorbed the scene, determined to take this memory back home with her. She had only a week left of her six-month stay in their home in Wimbledon.

Over the years, she had come to love Tom. She was embarrassed now at how she'd objected to Nisha marrying him. She couldn't accept a foreigner for a son-in-law. How could Nisha, from a small town in the Garo hills, cope with a man from London? Their marriage wouldn't last. But she had married him. And they had proved her wrong. And together they had created a beautiful little granddaughter for her. Divya, the light of her life.

She missed having Divya around on this visit. She had just gone to university that year. She came for a few weeks over the summer break but then took off again. Travelling with friends to music festivals. Camping out there in the mud and rain. She was also volunteering, knitting hats and scarves for a charity. And knitting prosthetic breasts, for women who lost theirs to cancer. Imagine that. Divya had shown Manju one of her creations, but she had felt too embarrassed to admire the fine handiwork. Especially when she had shown her the pink nippled woollen breast in front of her father.

'They look like pincushions,' Manju had said later, running her fingers over the pink woollen breast, the areola a brighter pink and pointy. 'Who would wear these, Divya?'

'They are very much appreciated, Nani,' she had said. 'They are in great demand.'

Manju thought guiltily about the one she had in her sewing box, which *had* been used as a pincushion. She made a mental note to remove the needles from it, and then do what with it? She didn't really know.

The phone rang. Tom picked it up, balancing it against his chin as he dished out the eggs. He was quiet while he listened. Then he walked out into the garden. Nisha looked out of the window, raising her eyebrows in question. Divya, he mouthed and turned his back to her.

Tom returned to the kitchen, scratching his chin, balancing the phone and coffee cup in one hand. Divya was not feeling too good, nothing to worry about she had reassured him. She had just cancelled her cycling trip to Wales and wanted to spend the week at home, especially since her grandmother would be leaving for India soon. Manju was pleased that Divya wanted to see her before she went. It had saddened her to realise that her granddaughter had more exciting things to do rather than spend time with her grandmother. Who knew when she would see her next? Immediately she began planning dishes she would cook to fatten her up. Tom said he would pick her up on the way back from work.

Manju and Nisha settled down to discuss the menu, before she too left for her afternoon shift at the hospital. Manju savoured the moment of sharing the kitchen space with the familiar smells of yesteryears. Of those peaceful days in the hills, when her husband was alive and goat meat was delivered fresh to the door. When travelling across oceans was still an improbable dream. When the local doctor was still interested in Nisha's hand in marriage. Those days, she sighed. Those days.

Manju took a stroll around the garden. It was a good year for growing, and the vegetable patch heaved with bounty. She twisted off young French beans and cut salad leaves, thinking of a last minute addition to the meal. The aroma of curried lamb wafted out, and she breathed it in deeply. If she shut her eyes, and kept still, this moment could be transported back to the time when she was a girl. And her mother's beef stew pulled her like a magnet from the playground to the dinner table every evening. Manju sighed. She hoped to create a sense of warmth and welcome for Divya the same way her mother had, all those years ago.

The gate clanged, and Divya walked in. She looked pale and drawn. She went up to Manju and embraced her. She inhaled her granddaughter's fragrance. She smelled of apples and honey. But she felt fragile, her skinny arms clunking awkwardly around Manju's ample waist.

'You need to fatten up, child,' Manju laughed, pinching Divya's arm playfully. 'All this running around doesn't do anyone any good. When did you have a proper home cooked meal? And I mean daal chawal sabzi. Not your fish and chips and burgers and pizzas. Didn't your mother teach you to cook?'

Divya smiled a little, but her eyes brimmed up.

'Why don't you make that for me, Nani? That's why I came back. So you could cook for me,' she said and a tear fell down her cheek. She turned and ran into the house, dragging her suitcase through the lawn. The wheels catching the mud and grass on the way.

'Are you ok, beta?' Manju called after her. 'Why didn't you wait for your father to pick you up?'

'I took the earlier train. I've texted him,' Divya said and disappeared into the house.

The afternoon passed slowly. Divya stayed in her room, Manju could hear the TV on full blast. What was the point of her coming if she didn't even want to spend time with me, she thought, a bit upset with Divya's cold behaviour. She was sure that it was only an excuse she gave her father. There was something else, but she couldn't figure out what. When Divya finally came down for lunch, her eyes were red and swollen. She hardly ate, picking at morsels of rice and then pushing the plate away. Manju tried to coax her, but failed. Divya didn't even look at the cauliflower pakoras, her favourite, steaming in a bowl in front of her.

'What's wrong, Divya?' Manju asked, sitting opposite her. 'You don't seem okay. Tell me, I'm your Nani, after all.' She reached out and stroked Divya's arm, tentatively following the raised vein up to her elbow.

Divya jerked her arm away. She opened her mouth to say something, but then rushed out from her chair and ran into the toilet. Manju heard her retching, and sobbing. No, it wasn't sobbing. It was a low keening sound that made her shudder. She knew that sound very well. And she understood.

Manju retreated further away from the toilet. She did not want to know. Her heart beat so fast, she was afraid of blacking out. What had that stupid girl done? Just at the threshold of her future, and now this? All those trips with her friends. All that freedom. She had known it was not right to give a young girl so much freedom. But how could she have said anything. Her parents had allowed her, and let her dig a hole into which she had fallen. Dragging the entire family with her. Her bright future was now smothered into darkness. She was ruined now.

Manju felt nauseous. The smell of the food in the kitchen made her feel sick. Her head was spinning, confusion and fear abound. She started to clear away the table. Something to keep her mind busy. The plates clattered as she threw them into the dishwasher. She scrubbed the kadhai in which she had fried the pakoras. Scrubbed until her fingers bled from gripping the steel wool so hard.

'Divya,' she shouted, throwing the pan back into the sink. 'How could you do this to yourself? How could you do this to your parents?'

She ran out into the garden, gasping for breath. The agapanthus swayed its lilac blooms in the breeze, oblivious to the tension around. Bright orbs of tomatoes hung from the vines. The roses spread their delicate fragrance throughout the garden. Manju was transported back home, to her haven where orchids grew wild. To her haven, where nightmares had once reigned. She wrung her hands in desperation. How could this happen? She would have to discuss it with the girl, see if they could make some sense out of it. Be strong, she commanded herself. Be strong.

Divya broke the news to her parents. Manju stayed up in her room, unable to face them, or the truth. She was afraid of the answers. She was afraid of Nisha's pain. Divya's pain. What of Tom? How would he react? Would he scream and shout and rain abuses on his daughter, never speak to her kindly again? Would he threaten to banish Divya from his sight? Would he force her to abort the baby? The very thought shook her soul. She clamped her teeth tight to stop herself from screaming. She tried to concentrate on listening downstairs. She could hear quiet voices, crying, but no shouting. Perhaps they were more civilised than she could ever be. Perhaps they had sorted a way out.

*

A week later, Manju's bags are packed. She's leaving. Going back home. There have been tears, reconciliation, forgiveness. A decision has been made. Divya has decided to have the baby. Nisha and Tom have promised to support her in every way. They want to meet her boyfriend. He'll come over before the autumn semester begins. They understand that it is difficult for Manju to accept such a thing. It is unacceptable where she comes from. But they don't understand, really. They don't know. She is relieved the baby is allowed to live. She will then, set her eyes on her first great-grand-child.

As Tom drives her to the airport, they sit silently in the car. She counts superstore lorries to take her mind off thinking. She hates these moments before separation. Will they meet again? She always wonders. The radio is tuned to Classic FM. The music soothes her. It is familiar music. Her father played the violin. Her father, who meant everything to her, has become a hazy image in her mind. But she can still hear him play Mozart's concerto number five. In front of the fireplace on cold, wintry nights, he played his music with utter dedication and love. She sees his silhouette against the fire, swaying as he plays.

But the music rises to cacophony. To the screams and anguish. To the excruciating pain. He played and played, to drown everything out.

Stop, oh stop, Manju grits her teeth, pressing her hands to her ears. I don't want to hear this. Tom flicks off the radio. He looks at her and asks if she is okay. Manju's breathing is shallow. She leans back and tries to calm down. Not now. Not now.

Tom drives into a service area and pulls up. She asks for coffee, and watches his back as he sprints across the car park. She feels a chill in the car, and pulls her cardigan closer. The sky is criss-crossed with planes, man-made shooting stars weaving patterns on the inky black canvas. And gracefully, like a dream from a far away time, the moon rises from behind the services.

Majestic and pure, floating up to the stars. She watches, mesmerised.

Her hands instinctively touch her stomach. She has always felt emptiness there. For months she had watched it grow, too afraid to accept what was happening. Maybe it would disappear. She would wake up one morning to find herself pure and untouched. Her body unchanged. But that was not how it was. Her body changed. The man who had forced himself on her, the watchman, disappeared without a trace. She believed they took him away and killed him. She never asked. They never told her.

The devil himself is inside you, her mother had cursed, watching her daughter writhe in agony as they tried their best to finish it off.

Manju remembers that time in third person. Like it had happened to someone else. She had indeed shifted out of her body, floating somewhere in the space directly above her, watching herself. Hating herself for letting it happen. But what could she have done?

A child without a father's name, growing inside her. A tumour, that had to be cut and got rid of. A shame never to be mentioned again. Who would have known that one day, in another land such things could be possible? That an illegitimate child could be accepted with love and dignity? She wished for that forgotten child, born so many years ago, such love. Such acceptance. For she was born out of violence and fear. And when she was born, they took her away. She never got to hold that baby. But she remembers that face. It comes to her in her dreams, even today. That face, like the harvest moon, slipping out of her reach. Out of her life and disappearing into nowhere. Somewhere. She never knew where.

Her parents never spoke about that child. It was as if she had never existed, never appeared on their horizon that night, on the twenty-fifth of May, when the owls hooted among the trees, and the wolves bayed in the distant hills. It was as if that bloodstained mattress never bore the proof of her pain. It burned silently in the backyard, thin wisps of cotton catching the summer breeze. Making the air smoky and stinging the eyes. Her swollen body, leaking milk and tears, healing slowly behind the heavily barred door of the servant's room. The reality transforming into a dream. The evidence disappearing into thin air.

And once again she is at a loss. The face she has sought after all these years, the tiny face that had looked up at her for a few moments, recognising her as the mother, has appeared in Divya's womb once more.

Tom returns with two Styrofoam cups. He asks if she's okay. He looks quite shaken by her earlier reaction. He tells her not to worry about Divya. He gives her his word that he will protect and care for her, and help support the baby to the best of his ability. She must find it in her heart to forgive Divya and embrace the situation. It will be better that way.

She touches his arm in gratitude, and blesses him. You are a kind man for understanding your daughter's situation, she reassures him and points to the moon. Such is God's creation, she says. Unblemished. Perfect in every way. They sit in silence, watching the moon, the coffee steaming in their hands.

They reach the airport. Before getting out, Manju takes Tom's hand in hers. Thank you, she says. You are precious, my son. Look after your family – our family – well. He embraces her. Holds her to him like a child who needs confidence and strength from his mother. She gives him all she has, squeezing out every ounce of goodwill from her body. She takes off her gold chain with the diamond solitaire, her mother's, and slips it into his hand.

For Divya's child, she says. My great-grand-child. My little piece of that moon.

Smile Harder
Richard Smyth

'Thanks for seeing me,' he says.

    'No problem, Inzamam.'

    'But it *was* a problem. Don't say that when I'm saying thank you. Say "you're welcome". Don't say it like it's nothing.'

    Pause. Take a breath.

    'Sorry. You're welcome.'

    'Okay.' He shifts in his seat, nods. 'Okay.'

    'So – how are you doing, Inzamam?'

    'I'm doing bad, aren't I. Otherwise I wouldn't have called you, would I.'

    'No, I see that. Do you want to tell me what happened?'

    'My head's just all over the place, man. It's like popcorn.'

    'Like – sorry, what?'

    Impatiently: 'Like a packet of popcorn, when you microwave it. Rattling, all the time rattling, banging. Only the microwave never goes *ping*, it never stops, it's never finished. Pop pop pop. All over the place.'

    'Is there anything in particular bothering you?'

'Everything! Everything. Wife. Daughter. Father, mother, brother. Both brothers.' He smiles quickly. He has a nice smile. 'Money, bills. The news, the TV. Traffic! Women. God.'

'But nothing more than usual?'

'*Everything* more than usual.'

I nod, take a note, just for form's sake.

'And tonight – did something happen tonight, Inzamam? Before you called us?'

'I was just driving. Out to Birstall, on a delivery. Guy had ordered chicken jalfrezi and a Peshwari naan. Peshwari naan! With a jalfrezi! And I was driving, and I was just thinking, man, what's wrong with you man, Peshwari naan, with a jalfrezi. Are you crazy. So I was just thinking about that and then I started thinking about what I'd say to him when he answered the door, if I'd say, "Listen man, are you crazy or what, you don't order a Peshwari naan with a chicken jalfrezi, you want a garlic naan, or chapati, that's what you want, innit? Not Peshwari." And then I thought, what's he going to do when I tell him this? I pictured him, this guy with his stupid food, I pictured him just shutting the door in my face. Like I was a nobody, man. Maybe he'd say something, like, "Thanks, chief", all sarcastic or something, or maybe he'd laugh at me, like right in my face. I thought about that and I just started getting so mad. Just at my imagination! Pop pop pop. It wasn't just the jalfrezi. It was everything. Everything.'

Dry throat. Swallow. Nod.

'What did you do, Inzamam?'

'Don't look at me like that, man. I didn't do anything.'

'I mean – what happened?'

'Nothing happened. I pulled over, on the hard shoulder. Stopped the car. Just sat there.'

'Were you still thinking about the man with the curry?'

'Wasn't thinking about anything. Couldn't think, man. Pop, pop, pop. Like having the radio on dead loud but no music coming out, no one talking, nothing being broadcast. Just loud noise.'

'And then what did you do?'

'I called the number you gave me. I came here.' He laughs. 'The jalfrezi's still in the car, if you're hungry. Be cold but it's still good.'

Mirror his smile.

'Won't the customer be upset when his dinner doesn't arrive?'

'Can't worry about him, man. Should cook his own dinner anyway. People today. Want everything brought to them. Click their fingers, want people to come running.'

'We're a service economy these days, they say.'

'You don't know anything about it.'

'You clicked your fingers tonight, didn't you, Inzamam? And I came running.' Smile. Smile harder. 'Just another branch of the service industry.'

Oh no—

'You don't know *anything* about it!' He sweeps his arm across my desk. Crash. Laptop, coffee cup, calendar. Coffee on my shoes. Heart's hammering.

Straight away he says: 'It's okay. I shouldn't have done that. Don't talk to me like that. You don't know what it's like. But it's okay. I'll go. Sorry. You made me angry. Sorry. It's okay.'

'What are you going to do?'

Whatever it is, don't do it here, don't do it to me.

But he won't do anything. I can see that much.

'I'll go home,' he says. 'I need to sleep, man. Sorry, Doctor. I'll go home, go to bed. I'll go home.'

He goes. I guess he goes home. The main thing is, he goes.

*

New day. No time for a shower. Coffee in a paper cup. 'Rachel', the guy writes on the cup. It's Róisín but never mind. Bus, train, bus. Then a walk. Halfway house on the edge of an industrial park.

'Morning, Ro.' Ken's the day warden.

'Everyone here?'

'Everyone as should be, nobody as shouldn't.'

Six men here, plus Ken. All men with 'issues'. All except Ken, although he's probably got issues of his own. Who hasn't? Six men with sex issues, social issues, violence issues. Mad men, you'd have called them once. Six mad men and me.

Weak tea, milk on the turn. Cereal bar. Sofa in the warden's office, box-file on my knee, wrestling with paperwork. Pirate radio station playing hip hop down the corridor. Get this done then go round and inspect the troops. Glance over the register: Jim, Anwar, Craig, Raheem, Lee, Patrick.

130

Lee put his wife in hospital. Anwar ran over a prostitute and drove off. Craig came out of the army and tried to rape a schoolgirl.

Issues.

I'd have said it was mad, once. Me? In here? With them? Overnight?

Now, it's nothing. I don't mean that it's not frightening. I mean that being frightened is nothing.

Rounds. Psychologist face on. Jim shakes my hand with both of his, smiles. Lots of nodding, affirming, agreeing. Out on a job today. Plasterer. Cash-in-hand I reckon. Don't begrudge it. Patrick, older, slower. Can't smell booze on him. The others in Psych hate him. He rants, raves, throws chairs. Broke Hannah's hand. OK with me or OK so far anyway. That's why they assigned him to me.

Raheem monosyllabic under a bandanna. Lee jumpy, twitchy. Scab on his bald head.

Anwar's new, shy. Booked up today with appointments, advisors, counsellors.

'They're not as scary as they sound,' I say.

'I'm not scared,' he says.

Sure, Anwar. Me neither.

Tesco Express lunch, back to the hospital. Half two, erectile dysfunction. Half three, AIDS. Half four, grief, or depression, or both. Those are the goodies. Couple of hours to myself, read a journal article, eat an apple.

Cath puts her head round the door.

'You look knackered.'

'I am knackered.'

'Chin up.'

Gone. Back to the baddies.

Late round at nine. Dark outside. Clipboard. Jacket. Psychologist face. *Psychologist face.*

There's a secure room downstairs where I sleep and there's a lock on the door but there's no lock on me, now, doing the rounds up and down the wan-lit corridors. Signs are all I have: go away, stop, back off. No. *No.*

Jim's 'ready to turn in', 'dead beat'. Plaster-dust in his hair. Raheem in a plastic chair with a Bible and a fag. Might be a spliff. Think it's a spliff. Don't care. G'night, Raheem. Lee wound up. He wants to talk I think but I'm not talking to him. Not at night. I'm friendly in the mornings – I do my *job* in the mornings – but not at night.

Anwar doesn't recognise me from this morning. Another weary white face. Whatever. Dead on his feet. Waves me away.

I leave Patrick till last because his room's nearest my room.

'Good day?'

'A good day,' he nods.

I don't get near enough to smell if he's had a drink. If he's had a good day he probably has.

'G'night Patrick.'

'Goodnight, Róisín.'

I don't like that. 'Doctor' is something I have. One of my signs, one of my best ones. Pause at the door. Put him right? *Doctor Baines, to you.* No. Never mind. Go.

Close his door behind me.

Then the lights go out and I hear the door open again.

There's a light switch at the far end of the corridor, by the door downstairs, and there's one a few paces back the way I've just come. That's the one Patrick's tripped.

Run.

A footstep bends the floor tiles. Breath on the back of my neck. Don't run. Too late. Fight? No. Not yet. Half-turn my head. Breath: whisky breath. Patrick a pace away. Arm's reach.

Think. Patrick's history: booze, anger, depression. Brawler, rough sleeper. Nothing *bad*. Women? Don't know.

He's holding his breath. You do that before you jump off the high board.

'Patrick,' I say.

I hear him swallow.

I have my jacket, my clipboard, my psychologist face. No use now, here in the dark.

'Patrick,' I say. 'I don't know what you're thinking of doing. But if you do anything to me, you'll be back with Hannah. And you hate Hannah.'

Stupid. Stupid. Why would that stop you? If you were going to kill someone, rape someone, beat someone up, why would that stop you?

The floor tiles flex. Run. No. Wait.

I hear the door open. I hear it close. No breath. Turn. Still a booze smell. His smell. Wait. Wait.

Then run, run like hell, hammer the light switch, turn, gone?, gone, empty corridor, bash at the keypad, hammer and kick at the door, blunder through, slam shut, slam again, down the stairs, into the overnight room, light on, slam shut, lock.

Stop. Breathe. Think. Me and Cath will laugh about this. We hate Hannah too. Breathe. Breathe. Drink in the light.

*

'Better, I think. Thank you. Better. A bit better.'
'That's good.'
'Yeah.'
'How do you feel about – about last time, Inzamam?'
Squirms in his chair.
'Sorry, doctor. Obviously. It's up one minute down the next. Do something bloody daft one minute then the next – you know. Sorry.'
'It's okay.' No. Correct myself. 'Well, of course, it wasn't okay, Inzamam. But I know you know that, and I appreciate your apology.'
A grin. Then suddenly no grin.
'I wouldn't hurt you,' he says.
He wants me to say 'I know'.
'Good.'
'Never. I'm not like that.'
'Good.'
He looks around the office.
'Bloody mess in here.'

'I know. That's what you get when five doctors share an office meant for one.'

'That's what I'm like. Chaos. Stuff all over the place. I mean in my head, you know. All sorts of stuff. Enough stuff for five people. Five hundred people! And it's funny because everywhere else I'm very tidy, doctor, I'm proper tidy!' A laugh. 'And I always think one day I'll tidy it all up and throw out all the rubbish and that and it'll be okay, like a nice place to live.'

'Well, that's what we're here to help with.'

'But the thing is, doctor.' Leans forward, folding his hands. His leather jacket creaks. 'I don't want to throw out the wrong stuff. How do I know? How do I know what's worth something?'

'What do you think is the most valuable thing you have? Personally. What are you most afraid of losing?'

'Daughter. Mum. Car. Wife. House. But in my head? I don't know. It's like, anger. Anger can be good, can't it? It's good to be angry – at injustice, bad things, sin.'

'Perhaps it's about learning to control these things. Rather than getting rid of them.'

'Should learn to control my wife.' Another grin. 'Fat chance. But then if you can control it's not anger, is it, though. I don't know what it is. It's like – love.' Spoken shyly. Grow up, for Christ's sake. 'I don't know how you control it. You're not meant to. I don't want to, sometimes.'

'What about fear, Inzamam?'

A frown. Not angry. Puzzled.

'I dunno.' Now a laugh. Something like a laugh anyway. 'What would I be scared of, man? But I suppose if my house was on fire or someone was coming after me with a big gun or something – being afraid tells you to run, doesn't it? Get out, get away. Bad things are happening.'

Nod. Make a meaningless note.

'If you control your fear,' Inzamam says, 'you'll just, like, stay there, like an idiot, while your house burns down.'

Smile.

'Some might call that brave.'

'Some might, if they're an idiot.'

Laugh.

The Dancers

–

Constantinos Andronis

The Dancers
Constantinos Andronis

I was born and raised in Eleusis, Greece. I have studied Philosophy yet art has always evoked a deeply rooted emotional response. As has music and poetry. I should think that Philosophy has enabled me to view things beyond their finite structure, to seek beyond the form and surpass the perspective of mere depiction; this process formed my perception of the world – the inner and the outer – and is an apparent characteristic of my art.

I am perplexed by and forever seeking to embrace the sempiternal question on the 'self' in its unique, metaphysical and existential presence. What makes me, me? In this attempt to approach the complexity of the interweaving yet unique 'self' my art visits the notion of the fragility of the self and reflects on the solitude of togetherness. I do not seek to describe or illustrate through my art; I see art as a means to transcend beyond the seen, beyond the visual and through this journey of transcendence to evoke, provoke and ponder on the vital questions of the being.

Art, for me, is a psychic protolanguage.

The Dancers (2016 - ongoing)

I often think of my Dancers series as poems; as connected, resonant words. Each stroke bears its own spacial uniqueness and carries an inherent visual stimulus. The Dancers balance on their fluidity and the interweaving strands denote an amalgam of memory and existence.

Enamel on paper (40.5×30.5)

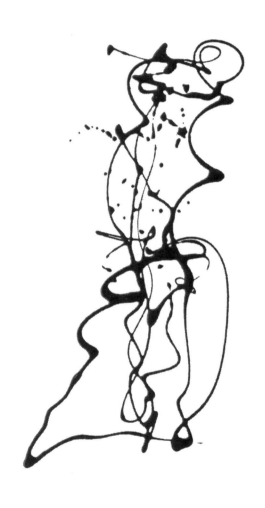

144

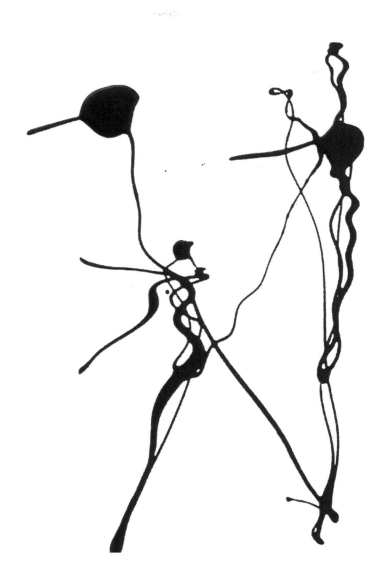

147

Three Poems
Ingrid Casey

Molly Bloom goes to yoga

Yes I made three hearts, and hinted at one more, no
I don't feel like writing about scourges or gyres or
changes or art because today the writing is about
laminar flow, aquatic claim on phallic, no tumult or
smashing or sloshing but a clear glass, illusive stream,
the knowledge that during savasana there are thousands
of possible hearts skipping about the room, there are hands
touching your hands, the sacred hands the veined vascular
moments of magic the carpet is rough you are supine you
are released you don't need politics or whisky or edgy shit
and you're as much of a poet as Hector or Roland and you
listened to Herbert about always questioning and your clown's
face, you still love makeup but you understand that reality is
the thing we dream into being and truth is a light in the navel.

Millennials

I go to Hades once a month, to check if I'm still
alive. I look up at the roots of the trees; ash, oak,
lyme; these subterranean lungs, broccoli, bronchioles.
There are thirty-five nationalities in the incoming class;
gender is fluid, words flow, two and a half
decades cracked open the sternum of this land. This is
the healing, the salt has fallen out of the
letters, where once each consonant held bile, a scum
floating on the surface of solicitors' diatribes. No ripple
of truth, so my liver told, pushed down on solar plexus
every drop of gall incurred, curs, hurls, thighs, cars, boys,
men, schoolyards, stockrooms, shady Shelerin road, places
where gangsters were felled, crashed trees made the news,
but not the attempt to rape, to silence me on a post-session
Saturday. The tiger's roar of that decade screamed louder than
goodness. I release my silence, and write; a lustration. Setting
my daughter's star on the arc of the roots, I make this map, a
guide for her to live across inches, circumferences,
among standing trees, overland.

The Gambler misses his Mother

He lost his accent in a hurry, he lost it in the grounds
of the cathedral, sleeping rough three weeks after he
arrived, he lost it in lines and in the shoes of strippers,
he lost it in the stream of steam as a barista, he lost it in a
machine, on paper slips in the bookies, he lost it in cars,
maternity wards and in the pupils of his sons, those dilating
cameras fixed upon his mark, he lost it in stars seen from
bridges he thought would be the one he'd jump from, he
lost it on the first flight, he lost it at the beach on the run
as a teen, he lost it when his dad left him, he lost it when
he left his sons, he lost it in the pants of all the women he
seduces, he lost it in mirrors, in lakes where his limbs swim
free, he lost it when they sent him away, he lost it in bottles
at basketball games under beds in sheds, he lost it in every
boat he's fished from, he lost it on canal banks and in the soft
lighting of all the restaurants, he lost it in the tills he steals
from, he lost it in friendless pockets, he lost it in rehab among
the lushes, he lost it in the rushes of rivers, he lost it while
fucking, he lost it watching phone porn every day, he lost
it in churches, at meditation, he lost it out running swiftly, he
found it Skyping his mother. He found it during brief weeks
back home, none of his countrymen here can do the conjuring, only she
holds the key to the box of secrets, memory; the pool in
which his old self swims, surfaces. She's water, she's
giving him life. He's born in her garden, he's normal there, single
weeks at a time. It trips, trails from trouser hems on the return.

Colours
Nora Shychuk

Whoever got her ready for this did a piss poor job. Fake tan. Blood red wig. Too much make-up. If she was alive, she'd kill me. She looks fake – worn and dead and empty. When I touched her hand earlier it was cold and rubbery. I don't know why I was surprised, I just hoped it would have been different.

The house will be a mess when I get back. Dirty dishes and laundry and unpaid bills. The dog will probably have shat in the corner again and be whimpering by the door.

And then I think of her – of buying the house and her bright blue eyes and her raking leaves in the backyard. She wore my grey sweatshirt and when she came back inside she smelled smoky. Like the trees. Like autumn. When she hugged me her cheeks were still warm.

I think of her gardening. Or playing catch with our youngest. She had a hell of an arm until she got sick and lost weight. I watched from the window as she threw the ball and Caleb laughed. She never saw, but I was there. Just looking.

Her spaghetti sauce. She didn't tell me the recipe and now I won't know how to make it for the kids. I meant to ask, but it never seemed like the right time. Maybe it's on one of her recipe cards. Maybe it's on a scrap of paper in the room. Maybe—

'Dan. How are you?'

Pastor Aşlan is suddenly in my face and smiling.

'I'm okay, Alan.'

'John will be giving his speech soon. If you'd like to say anything after—'

'I don't think I can. The kids. I don't want to break down—'

He puts an arm on my shoulder as if to say he understands, but his overweight wife is in the corner and I know he doesn't get it.

What is life at the end of the day? Is it playing catch with your son? Or cooking spaghetti? Or gardening and watching as your tulips start to bloom and burst with colour? Is it watching your kids grow? Is it buying a house with a pine tree in the back and putting a birdfeeder on the maple for hummingbirds? Is it setting the coffee maker to wake up to the smell every morning? Is it your morning walks together before the kids wake up? Is it going to sleep next to the person you love?

I want to ask Pastor Alan what it all means, but I don't see the point.

Back home my bed will be cold and the girls will be crying and Caleb will keep asking for mommy and then he'll start screaming. Somehow, I need to stay close. Her address book is still by the bed. In her quick scrawl are the numbers of friends, family, doctors. Her clothes are in the closet. The girls will want to keep some and I'll keep the grey sweater. My sweater that became hers.

I look across the crowded room and see my daughter. She is faking it. Standing up too straight and shaking everybody's hands – and that *dress*.

I can't breathe in this thing. Mom bought it for me last Easter, the fabric dark green with a row of white flowers along the neckline; it's tight around my hips and I wonder if it's too short. I hate this. I hate the people here that pretend to care.

All I can think about is what she said to me in the hospital a couple nights ago. Dad said it was the chemo. It made her angry. The cancer in her lungs spread to her brain. It was eating her alive.

Still. She said it. I had a bad day at school and complained and she looked at me with such hate. Her eyes were slits and she pointed a bony finger at me. How did she put it? *I never liked you, Anna* or *I don't like you, Anna* or something like that. Dad told her to stop. He told her she didn't know what she was saying. She kept staring at me. Her lips were red and glazed with her spit. Her cheeks sunk inward. Eyes lined with yellow crust. Then she started crying and coughing and couldn't talk any more. There was a card on her lap from some lady that visited earlier and mom grabbed it. She looked at dad and pointed to the pen clipped to his shirt pocket. He gave it to her and she wrote on the pretty, aqua-coloured paper and handed it back to him. Dad tried to hide it but I could see the words in smudged, black ink.

I'm going to die here, aren't I?

He ripped up the card and told her to sleep. After a few ragged breaths she did, her face a mess of hard lines and pale skin.

People keep coming up to tell me that I'm the woman of the house now and that I'll have to help dad. Watch out for Caleb and Lauren, too. I think of singeing Lauren's neck this morning and how she screamed and for the first time all day I think I might cry.

Mom didn't die that night in the hospital. She got to come back home. The night before she died she was giggly and ate cookies in bed. She told me a story about her friend from college who slept with their Anatomy instructor and after he told her all of the scientific names for her body parts. Mom laughed so hard milk came out of her nose. We fell asleep and then she woke up in the middle of the night wheezing and choking. Dad was asleep in the chair but jumped up when he heard her cough. He tried but it wasn't enough. Mom's breathing slowed and then fell away altogether. She breathed in and never breathed out.

She had seemed so alive and dad told me that's what happened at the end. A last bit of strength. The body giving the soul all it has. But mom was tired, so she let go.

I see Ellen, my cousin, talking with her parents. It dawns on me then that I won't call for her any more. I won't say the word. I mouth it to myself. *Mom.* My throat feels like it's full of marbles.

Back at school people will hug me and bring me cards and candy for a week or maybe more and then it won't matter.

I haven't been up to the casket, but I've seen her from a distance; her white skin is ghostlike. I keep waiting for her to sit up and find me in the crowd.

Then there are arms around me. I turn and aunt Cheryl is plump and perfumed and dressed in black. She kisses my cheek with her dark purple lips.

'You were her first baby. Her first daughter. You look just like her, Anna.'

I say nothing and wish I could fly away.

'Ask your dad about her journal from when you were born. Your footprints. A cast of your little hand. Your birth announcement. She wrote letters to you. All those memories.'

My heart swells and suddenly mom is all around me. My mind jumps back to a memory of my own – to the time we went to Lake Erie Park and she taught me how to fish and cast my line. She packed ginger ale and peanut butter and jelly sandwiches. We didn't leave until the sun fell behind the trees. The light was yellow and warm and sparkled on the water.

'Want to get seats? John is going to speak in a minute,' Aunt Cheryl says.

I ask her to sit away from the first row and she nods because she understands. As we sit, I look for Lauren but can't find her.

Mom is so still. Her face is stretched and she wears too much blush. Her green shirt clings to her arms and she won't smile and she won't open her eyes. I think of going up to see her again but there is a line now so I stand to the side with a box of tissues in my hand. It isn't until Aunt Grace comes up to me that I notice I'm crying.

'It's okay, Lauren,' she says as she wipes under my eyes. I flinch and she hugs me even though I don't want her to.

'God has a plan,' she whispers into my ear.

'What is it?' I ask.

She leans back from me and smiles.

'You are an angel. An absolute angel.'

'Her hair is so red,' I say.

'What?'

'She didn't have any hair left.'

'Lauren.'

I look and see Papa Ben and Uncle Rob and they are both bald too but they're still here. Something in my chest gives way and I feel the hot tears again. Aunt Grace takes my hand and pulls me away from mom and over to dad. He leans down and takes my tissues and wipes them across my face too hard. Aunt Grace whispers to him and he frowns.

'Why don't you run to the bathroom and clean up a bit, honey? Try and relax.'

Dad hugs me and his beard is prickly against my face. I shrug him away and run with my head down. I hope nobody sees me cry.

The bathroom is pink and there is heart-shaped soap near the sink. I grab some, sniff it, and put it back, then I turn the knob with the red 'H' and cup my hands under the faucet until they fill and I splash the water all over my face. It drips down my neck and onto the lacy collar on my dress.

I look in the mirror and my eyes are still red. I blink and try to get rid of it but it stays. I put a little water on the tip of the soap and scrub under my eyes but it makes everything worse so leave and everything stings.

The carpet in the hallway is soft with colourful swirls of red and green and gold. My little white heels dig in and I sink as I walk. I come to the door where mom is but there are so many people around her that I don't think I can go in. I sit in a hard wooden chair just outside and even from there I can smell all the flowers by mom. The smell is too heavy and it makes my stomach hurt. Flowers are supposed to be outside in the grass or in mom's garden and I don't think I like flowers any more. Cousin Luke comes over and sits next to me and puts a hand on my shoulder. He tells me my hair is shinier than he remembers and that it looks very nice curled and down. I tell him Anna did it for me this morning, but I leave out the part where she accidentally burned my neck. The mark is covered and I don't want anyone to see.

Luke stretches out and leans back. He is eighteen and grown up and knows how to play the guitar. He is here with his sisters and his mom and dad. My stomach starts to hurt again. Luke puts a hand on mine and squeezes it.

'She loved you a lot.'

I want to ask him why he gets to keep his mom and I don't. The swirls on the carpet start to move and twirl and I notice there is purple mixed in with the gold and silver spots between the reds and the greens. I feel very sick. Something stabs me inside. I bring my hands to my stomach and close my eyes.

I wasn't there when it happened. I was at Kelly's for a sleepover and before I went mom looked like she didn't want me to go but I went anyway. Dad called me the next morning and said he'd be there soon to pick me up. He walked through the door and had snow on his coat and hat and brushed it on the floor. I thought that was rude because the snow would melt and it would be wet and cold on Kelly's feet. He came over to me but did not look at me. My hands shook and he said I needed to go home and I did and then I had to say goodbye.

After a while I go back into the room with Luke. Uncle John is at the front of the room and everyone is sitting down. Luke takes my hand and points to a couple chairs in the back corner and I follow. Uncle John keeps coughing and clearing his throat. He holds a yellow piece of paper in his hand. Mom is behind him. She doesn't move and I know she'll never move again.

How does this all look to Caleb? Where did he go?

Mommy won't look at me even though I touch her hand with daddy. She is very tired. Her skin feels like Play-Doh and I poke it until daddy tells me to stop. He moves me away from mommy so I try to go back but he takes my hand and says other people need their time with mommy. He holds my hand too hard and pulls me away but I'm not going fast enough so he picks me up and I am floating above everyone like a superhero.

I yell and laugh and Uncle Gerry looks up at me and his cheeks are wet and I reach out to him and he takes my hand but then lets go and turns away from me.

Daddy sets me down away from the crowd and Aunt Iris hugs me. She wears lots of necklaces and they poke my skin. She pulls me closer and she is wrinkly. Mommy isn't that wrinkly but Aunt Iris can still move much better than mommy can. She sits down and sets me on her lap.

'Your mommy said you were her sunshine, Caleb. Do you know that?'

160

I shake my head and squirm and wish she'd put me down. 'Do you know the song? You Are My Sunshine?'

She puts my head against her heart and I hear the thump, thump, thump as she starts to hum.

I close my eyes and see mommy at the sink. She wasn't supposed to be out of bed but she got up and walked to the bathroom and I found her as she was falling back so I yelled and yelled and daddy ran in and mommy screamed.

Daddy caught her just in time. He kissed me on the head and said thank God, thank God. All she had was a cut on her head from the side of the sink and it was only a little red. Daddy cleaned it and mommy said she loved me and cried and daddy put her back into bed.

I leave Aunt Iris and the room is very full and people are laughing and talking too loud and I am squeezing through as best I can. Someone steps on my foot so I run away. I look for Anna or Lauren but I can't find them. Where is daddy? I think of calling for him – or for mommy – but I don't think they'll hear me.

Then I hear a piano and the room gets very quiet but I keep moving and everyone is looking down and hiding their faces and I start tugging on their pants and skirts to make sure they are okay but they just look at me and smile but it is not a happy smile. It is not real. Some wave me away or tell me to find daddy or sit down like a good little boy.

I make it to the front and daddy is standing by mommy. His face is very red and tangled and I haven't seen it like this before. Uncle Marc stands with his arms around daddy. They

look stuck together. I look behind them and mom is still asleep.
She is still there.

*

Caleb is sleeping in his little bed with his rocket ship sheets and a
glow-in-the dark, starry blanket. He won't wake. He will hear in
the morning. Caleb. My little boy. I'm sorry to go. I barely got to
know you.

My throat is burning. Dan holds my head and I sip water
from a cold glass. Anna stands rigid at the far end of the room.

I want to tell them to help Lauren. She is sensitive and
tender-hearted. She will have trouble in school and won't make
many friends. Boys will pick on her and she will take it badly.
Stand up for her. Make sure the DVD player is working and hook
up the damn speakers already, Daniel. For her movies. Indiana
Jones and Star Wars and Cinderella. Make sure you hug her. Hug
her more than the other two and don't feel bad about it. She
needs it.

I cough and I feel a rip in my throat; I taste the blood,
sweet and salty all at once.

Anna. My little woman. Give her space to read her books.
Let her stay out on the hammock. All night. She is almost grown.
Don't be intimidated by her. She is so advanced, so passionate.
Mr Amentas told us that at teacher conferences last year,
remember? She will change the world, won't she? Let her go. Let
her see the world. Let her be angry. Let her bring boys home.
Walk her down the aisle on her wedding day. When you look at
her, think of me. Think of when it was us.

I gasp for air. My heart pounds in my chest. Dan moves the water away and sits down. He holds my hand.

His fingers. Rough and warm. Things start flashing and I see him pumping air into my tyres and then suddenly we are walking in downtown Philadelphia. He just gave me his hat because it started to snow. His ears are red and I reach out and they are cold to the touch. We are climbing a weeping willow by a lake. Where are we again? Georgia? Why were we... Why were we there? The flashes get faster. Hot chocolate. A blue jay. A spool of pink thread. Anna vomiting at the top of Niagara Falls. Christmas presents. Dan's paper cut. Blood on tape. Lemonade on mom's porch. My ballet shoes. Things spiral out of order.

Lauren falls and skins her knee. Dan runs after our dog down the street. My dress from my first semi-formal dance, hideously orange and frilly and glittery. Fireflies in jars. Caleb's head in my lap. Weeds in the garden. Wind in the trees. The oil lamp on the kitchen table. Bumblebees. Thanksgiving turkey. Sunlight through the curtains. The church bells ringing at noon. Fishing with the cold current on my calves.

Then I am very calm. My heartbeat slows. My breathing falls. In, then out. It is late now and I swear I can feel the blood in my veins as it tries to rush. Then all the colours. Every colour in the world – every colour I've seen and some that I haven't seen before – fills my head and I close my eyes. I do not think I am breathing any more. I just see, see, see...

Cat in a Bag
Tony Bianchi

Robert Stitch is ten years of age and lives at 51 Spence Place. He likes living at 51. It's a prime number. Mr Carr has just taught him about prime numbers at school and he thinks, Yes, that's us. Nothing can divide us. And another thing: that's how many houses there are in his street. Fifty-one houses, all two at a time, except for Mrs Kinleyside's bungalow, and the Stitches' house the last before you get to the waste ground. So, fifty-one on the door and fifty-one in the street. You reach the Stitches and you can't go any further, not in house terms. That's the end. Or the beginning, of course, depending on which way you're walking. But one or the other, not just lost somewhere in the middle of things.

Fifty-one houses. And one hundred and sixty-eight people, at the beginning, or nearly the beginning, because it took Robert a while to count them all, to make sure it was right. But the total kept changing then because some moved out and others moved in, some had babies and some died. Mrs McKenna next door, for example. She did both. She had a baby but then died straight afterwards, so same number, but different people. And a baby counts as much as anybody. Just a wee mite, but counts the same.

Then the names. Fifty-one houses but only forty-eight names, because there are McKennas in number 26 as well, and

Pantrinis in 12 and 49, and Quinns in 18 and 27, although, as far as Robert recalls, they aren't related. The Quinns, that is, not the others. So, forty-eight families, if you allow families of one, if you think one person can be a family. No cohabiting, either, not in those days. Just the odd lodger maybe, now and again, to put a spoke in the wheel. But anyway, Stitches at the end, guarding the fort, holding the line against the waste ground, the old pit-heap, the clumps of nettles and brambles, the dog dirt. Against Neil Barber from number 4, too, you might say, hanging out in the scrubby trees at the top, smoking roll-ups with his mates. No, you can't see them, not from 51, you'd have to walk over to do that, take the path through the nettles and the brambles and the dog dirt and clamber up the bank. And you'd not see them even then, not right away, you'd maybe just glimpse a curl of smoke floating up through the leaves, or catch a whiff of it on the air. But you'd know that was them. You'd turn back. Keep your distance.

And that's maybe when it starts. With Neil Barber. Not just number 51, the last house, that low brick wall the only thing left between the street and the nothing, but something bigger. Today Robert is taking the shortcut over the waste ground to visit his Uncle Jack. Uncle Jack lives on Verne Road and isn't his real uncle, but that's what his mam calls him, so Robert does the same. Jack is eighty and on Sunday afternoon he gives Robert a piano lesson. That's why he's carrying his school satchel. Inside is *Smallwood's Piano Tutor*, a compilation of scales, arpeggios and similar exercises, but with a few duets, too, simple things teacher and pupil can play together. Just the one book, but in the satchel all the same, to keep it clean, to show everyone that he's taking his studies seriously.

This, then, is the quickest way, if you want to get to Verne Road from Robert's house. Through the brambles, around the bottom of the pit-heap, past the concrete blocks where the pit shafts used to be, through some more brambles, then up the bank. And there you are. Verne Road. Ten minutes quicker than going round about. So that's the way he goes. That's the way he's gone every Sunday afternoon for the past two months. But today it's different. Neil Barber's there. Neil Barber, number 4, sat against a tree stump with one of his mates.

'What you got there?' he says. Neil Barber has a high, flutey voice. And his Adam's Apple goes up and down when he talks.

'Satchel,' says Robert.

'Show me.'

Robert holds up the satchel. He does as he's told, as the words tell him, no more, no less. Neil Barber says, 'Give it here.' And Robert obeys again because he doesn't know how not to. Neil Barber opens the leather straps, takes out the book and thumbs through the pages. 'Password,' he says. Then gives the book to his friend.

'What?' says Robert.

'Need a password to come this way. Can't take a book through here without a password.'

The friend is thumbing through the book now. Robert wants to tell him to mind his grubby fingers, to take care he doesn't crease the corners. But he knows that will only make matters worse.

'I don't know any passwords.'

'Can't come through, then. Not without a password.'

'But I've got... My Uncle Jack's waiting...'

Neil Barber shrugs, plays with the straps of the satchel, then looks around him. 'Alright, then. You'll get the password if you grab hold of that.' He nods towards the tall nettles just beyond his feet. 'That there,' he says, leaning over and pointing. 'Grab a hold of that.' Perhaps he thinks Robert doesn't know what a nettle is, what it does. Perhaps he's savouring the additional gratification of taking him by surprise.

Robert looks back down the bank. He looks over the waste ground, at his house on the corner. He thinks, if his mam comes out now he can make a run for it. He'll shout 'Mam!' He'll wave. And surely they won't stop him then, not when they see his mam. He waits, just a second or two, as long as he dares. He keeps his eyes on the front door, willing it to open. But Jean Stitch doesn't come out. Of course she doesn't. You can't make things happen just by thinking them. So he bends over. Just one move then. A quick lunge. Squeezes the nettle tight in his fist and lets go. Even though he's only ten he knows that's how you have to do it. 'Look, Robert,' his dad had said. And did it himself. Making him think he could take the pain. 'See?' And gritted his teeth. 'See that?' Making him think that's what men do. Grasp the pain. Show their sons how to grasp the pain.

Robert squeezes the nettle tight, and there's no sting, none to speak of, and Neil Barber isn't expecting that, he's expecting blubbering and whingeing. Robert squeezes tight and lets go. And because it's all over so quickly, Neil Barber doesn't have a password ready and all he can think of is 'Piss off!' In his flutey voice. His Adam's Apple going up and down. 'Piss off,' Robert says back to him. The other boy laughs. 'Piss off, piss off,' he cackles, as though that's the password, as though it's all a big joke. Neil Barber throws the satchel into the brambles. He takes the music book and throws that, too. Robert stands, mouth agape. Holds his breath. Feels a tight fist in his chest. But it's alright. There's no harm done. The satchel lands on top of a bush and the book misses the brambles altogether, opens up in the air, scatters its scales and arpeggios over a clump of dandelions. He runs over and picks up the music book first, because it's fragile and naked. The satchel at least has a skin, and a tough skin at that. He doesn't put the book back in the satchel, not yet. Best wait, he thinks. Best get moving.

When he reaches Uncle Jack's, Robert smooths out the pages, wipes a dead midgie from the cover. And he thinks, I won that one. None the worse, either, just a tingle in the fingertips, a green stain on the palm. Afterwards he goes back home the long way round. He goes the long way round both ways for a while after, too, knowing he won't be able to say 'piss off' again and get away with it.

Two months pass. Then Robert's new friend, Lauren, says, 'Let's go over the waste ground and look for forky-tales.' Lauren lives at number 20, between the Quinns and the Askews, and she isn't afraid of anything very much because her dad's a policeman. That's all she has to say – 'My dad's a policeman' – and the other kids look at her, wondering what she's going to tell her dad about them. Lauren hasn't been friends with Robert before because she goes to a different school, and anyway she's a girl.

But then her dad was in the *Chronicle*. Picture and everything. Caught some lads trying to burn down a chip shop in town. And Robert's glad she lives in his street. He'd be even gladder if she lived next door. But she doesn't, so that's why he says, 'Alright, then, you got a jam jar?' Keep in with the policeman's daughter, he thinks. Next best thing. So they go to look for forky-tales over on the waste ground, just the two of them.

But they only find the one, and Lauren says they have to let it go or it'll get lonely. So they look for ants the week after, and spiders the week after that. And when they don't find any proper spiders in the brambles or the nettles, just a couple of money-spiders, Robert says, 'Up in the trees. They'll be up there, making their webs in the branches, catching the flies.' So they clamber up the bank, Robert leading the way. And maybe Robert thinks it's alright today, because he has the policeman's daughter with him. Or maybe he doesn't want to show himself up in front of a girl. And anyway there's no smoke, not a whiff of it, and he thinks, alright then, go for it. They scramble about amongst the trees and Lauren has already started looking up in the branches when they hear the voices: Neil Barber's flutey whine and another voice, more of a mumble, that Robert doesn't recognise. They come through the gap in the trees, Neil Barber first, then the mumbler. And Robert sees that the mumbler is Gordon Pratt. Gordon Pratt doesn't live in his street. He lives above the pub on Stephenson Avenue and wears thick glasses and Robert only knows him because his younger brother goes to the same school. They walk through the gap and down the other side, down to the waste ground, the bricks and the concrete blocks. Gordon Pratt is carrying a sack over his shoulder and Robert can't understand why it's twitching. Swaying a bit as well, being swung over his shoulder, but twitching, too, little fidgets this way and that, all by itself.

That's when Lauren comes back from the spiders and says, 'What you looking at, Robert?' He says, 'Sssh!' But it's too late. Neil Barber's bony head turns round. He shouts, 'Who's that?' And then: 'Look who it is. It's Robert Stitch. What you doin there, Stitch?' Gordon Pratt mumbles something. And Neil Barber says, 'He's got a lass with him. Look. You playin with lasses now, Stitch? You just a big lass?' Robert can see his Adam's Apple going up and down, even from there, even from the top of the bank. 'Come down here, Stitch,' he shouts. 'I've got something for you.'

Robert considers cutting back through the trees and on to the road and back home the long way round. But Lauren says, 'You're not scared of them, are you?' And she sets off down the bank by herself, without asking. So Robert has to follow. When they get to the bottom Neil Barber's putting the sack on the ground. It's stopped twitching now but Robert can see a shape in it, an indeterminate lump, slightly bigger at one end than the other. 'Bet you don't know what's in there,' says Neil Barber. And Lara says, 'Twigs,' because she hasn't seen the bag twitching. 'Twigs and leaves.'

Neil Barber goes into the bushes and brings back a stick. He stands over the sack and pokes it and the twitching starts again. Just a quick little jump, a bit of a wriggle. Then nothing.

'You want a go?'

He holds out the stick. Lauren takes it from him. She taps the edge of the sack. Nothing. She places the stick gently on the bump in the middle. Nothing. She rubs the bump this way and that. The wriggling starts again. She jumps back. Watches. Waits. And nothing again.

'Waste of time, that, man,' Gordon Pratt says and picks up a stone. Just a little pebble. Lobs it at the sack, at the bump in the middle. And misses. Picks up a bigger stone.

'Don't do that,' Lauren says.

Gordon Pratt looks at her. 'Or what? Eh? What'll you do if I do?'

Lauren says what she always says. 'I'll tell my dad. My dad's a policeman. I'll tell him.'

Everybody stands still for a moment. Robert thinks, that's done it. They'll stop now and we'll get away. But then Neil Barber says: 'Tell him what?' And again. 'Eh? What'll you tell him?' Then, in a girly voice: 'Daddy, Daddy, they were throwing stones at a sack. Go and arrest them.'

Gordon Pratt laughs. And Neil Barber says, 'Go on, then. Go and tell your dad. Tell him we're throwing stones at a sackful of fuckin twigs.' Then he picks up a stone and throws it. It hits one end of the sack and bounces away. Gordon Pratt throws his own stone and hits the shape. There's a big jump, like the sack is trying to take off. And maybe there's a sound as well, but Robert can't make it out, because Neil Barber has thrown another stone, and another, and is shouting 'Bull's eye! Bull's eye!' and clapping his hands. But must have been. Some sound. Surely. A squeal. A yelp. With those stones landing, not every one, but enough. Hard stones through that thin sack. And no way out. And Neil Barber's got a handful now. Dat-dat-dat they go. And the odd one just a dull thwap, when it hits the shape. Gordon Pratt, too. He's gathered stones from by the concrete blocks. Dat-dat-dat-dat they go. Another thwap. And another. And is that a squeal? Or is that Lauren? Because that's when Lauren starts crying. Just a few whimpers. Then runs off across the waste ground. Says nothing more about her dad or anything else, just runs through the brambles and the nettles and doesn't look back.

They throw more stones. And the shape's just twitching now. Like it's trying to dig down into the earth, bury itself and the sack, out of harm's way. A scratchy sound, too, by now, as if the claws are coming through at last. But no sight of them. Still no squeal, either. Just scrape, scratch, scrape, scratch. Like cats do. Try to bury it all, the pain, the wound, the crying, everything Even offer you a little purr. Pretend all's well. Like camouflage. Right as rain, it says. Little purr. Away with you now, nothing to see here. Everything buried. And who's to say it's a cat? But what else? No squirrels around there. Not on the waste ground. And the stones still coming. Hitting the shape, too, because they've got their eye in. And anyway it's easier now the shape has stopped moving. Given up the ghost. Or maybe too broken. Out of it. Like Robert's mam with her migraine. Off to bed and not a peep for hours.

Gordon Pratt throws his last stone. Neil Barber only has bits of gravel left. He gives Gordon Pratt a couldn't-care-less look and chucks them away. Chucks them anywhere, not bothered with the sack any more. Pulls out his Rizlas and starts rolling up. Just his fingers moving. Nothing else. Just fingers. Although maybe, who knows, still a little twitch from the sack. Tiny flick. Like the flick of a tail. But the wind, more than likely. Curling the corner.

Robert walks over to the concrete blocks where the pit-head used to be. Nobody says anything. Lost interest in the sack. Lost interest in Robert Stitch. Just the fingers now, rolling the papers, thinking of the smoke, maybe just thinking of nothing. When he gets to the concrete blocks he looks around. Picks up a brick and drops it again. Too heavy. Too big. Picks up a broken brick, just a half brick, but as big as he can hold. Hands only ten, like the rest of him. But can reach the octave. Splay the thumb and fingers and bang out the two Cs. So Uncle Jack can say, 'You've got pianist's hands, right enough.' Still, just half a brick. To get a grip. Need to get a good grip. A half brick as big as an octave.

When he gets back Neil Barber is sat on the ground, drawing on his rollie. Gordon Pratt's still licking his Rizla. Robert thinks he catches a twitch in the sack. Barely that. Flick of a tail. If it has a tail. Flick of an ear. Three flicks together. Little tremble. Little flutter. The heart beating. Fast. Too fast. Maybe just the wind. Brick tight in his hand. And the shape still then. Just a quiver at the edge of the sack. The wind. Nothing but the wind. Brick tight in the hand. Shape dead still. But just a shape. And where? So down on his knees. Brick up in the air. But where? Tight in the fist. Then down hard. Anywhere. On the soft. Hard on soft. And then a jump. Yes, jump. You think the jumping is all over, nothing but a few quivers left. But no. A big jump. So that you jump yourself. The sack coming at you. The sack, the shape, everything. So brick up in the air again. And down. Harder this time. Up in the air. And down. Up and down. Brick digging into the hand now. So just once more. Up and down. And no jump left now. No, not a quiver.

Neil Barber says, 'Fuckin hell, man. Fuckin hell.' Gordon

Pratt just sits, stares, rollie in hand, not lighting up. Robert gets to his feet. Sees the stain on the sack. Little round stain. Like a half crown. Not red, either. Or at least more black than red. And he thinks, a black cat, then? Or is a cat's blood black? But spreading then. Just a bit. Not round any more. More a streak.

Robert drops the brick, turns and cuts through the trees, sets off for Verne Road and Uncle Jack. No password. Nothing. He doesn't look back. And he thinks, Yes, he's done right. Right by the cat. Or whatever. The shape. The sack. The jump and the twitch and the stain. Right by Uncle Jack. Not letting him down. And right by himself, too. Right by Robert Stitch, number 51, holding the fort, guarding the frontier. Except it should have been Neil Barber under the brick. Neil Barber in the sack. Twitching.

So next time. Doesn't know how, but next time. The cat first. But just the beginning.

Dazzle
Iain Robinson

It seemed to Lucian that there was almost nothing between him and the horizon. The sea had peeled back and the wet sands shimmered and calmed in the cool afternoon light. The waves were breaking nearly a mile out, on the first sandbar, and the wind ruffled the surface of the lagoon that had formed with the falling tide. Sometimes he would dare to wade into the shallows. He knew though that when the waters turned and began to run in, it was wise not be too far out.

He walked where the wet sands were firm and pocked with the holes and curling initials left by lugworms. The sun was low but he had the sense it was all around him, a glaring sheen on the flats and shallows. He had his field glasses around his neck and his camera bag slung over his shoulder, although this was strictly a casual walk, a way of giving Judith a bit of time on her own. He didn't expect to see anything special, just the usual coastal birds, but this was enough for him. In the distance, where the river ran out its diminutive estuary, he could just discern a cloud of oystercatchers, a dazzle of black and white plumage almost melting into the haze. This simple display left him breathless. Holding the glasses steady, he felt the shifting flock as though he were a part of it.

They had two more days in the cottage. It had been a mistake, he realised that now. Judith would want this again and he would have to call a halt to things. He would wait until the evening. There was a spare room made up with a single bed, he could sleep out the remaining nights there, or else leave, make up some excuse to tell Sally when he arrived home early.

As he pulled the binoculars away he became aware of two dogs bearing down on him, full of the rush of the wind and sea. He crouched to fuss them as they sniffed around his legs. A man, the owner, strode towards him and called them to heel. Lucian hadn't noticed them approach, he'd been too engrossed with the birds, or perhaps the light had tricked him, the glare of it off the sands. Lucian raised a hand in greeting, but the dogs were already pounding up the beach and the man shrugged apologetically and carried on after them.

Lucian felt a little relieved. He didn't want to talk. The landscape was enough. The wind was blowing dry sand off the dunes and across the wet flats. It blew like a snaking mist at ankle height, or perhaps, it struck him, more like a river, a wide river of dry sand, and its sinuous currents alive and alert around him. He'd met Judith the previous autumn in one of the hides on the marshes. She was younger than him, a little nervous, but they'd hit it off, and when he suggested a pub meal together that evening, she'd accepted. It wasn't the right thing to do, he knew that, but it had felt right, the way the estuary and the marshes felt right. The attention was flattering; he'd long ago given up on himself. Things had been tough for him and Sally.

He glanced over at the dunes and realised that he was straying further from the high tide mark. His route had taken him across the salt marshes and into the dunes before he'd struck out along the beach toward the estuary. The cottage overlooked the marshes. From the bedroom you could see right over to the sandbars. It meant that they could set up a camera with a tripod and telephoto and watch the birds from there. He wondered whether Judith would have seen him, and if she had followed his progress along the raised footpaths to the beach. The circular route would take him as far as the estuary and then along the back of the dunes to the village again. With luck by the time he reached the head of the estuary the waters would be on the rise, pushing the wading birds off the mud and back to their roosting places. She would only lose sight of him when he reached the estuary and the path went behind a line of trees. Of course, he realised, there was no reason to think she would be looking out for him.

He squinted into the wet sheen of the sands. He was well along the beach now and to his right, off the shore, he could see the rusted hulk of a freighter on the sandbank, broken in three. At high tide nothing of it showed except for the warning mast. There was a deep water channel into the estuary on the other side of the bank. A further channel ran between the bank and the beach, though it was shallow enough to wade out to the wreck at low tide. He could hear the cries, the distant yelps and shrieks, of black-headed gulls, the wind carrying the sound. He walked on, cutting across the sands towards the head of the estuary. The cries came back, keening and pleading. He looked out towards the sandbank. The water was moving in along the channel, the sun dancing white light off its surface. He shielded his eyes, wishing he'd brought his sunglasses. There was something. He couldn't be sure. The light seemed to move, the air thick with it, distorting. He told himself it was the head of a seal, they came up the channel sometimes. He screwed up his eyes. The head was gone, something else. It looked for a moment like an arm, a flash of red. He pulled his field glasses up to his eyes and scanned. Nothing. He felt his heart pumping. The wind dropped a little, and the cries returned. He knew that people got caught out, spent too much time with the wreck and found themselves cut off. The sandbank was already sinking below the waters. He dropped the binoculars from his eyes and squinted into the dazzle. For a moment he saw the outline of a man, chest deep in water, then nothing again. He could have stumbled, gone under. Lucian waited for him to appear. He did not. Lucian looked back at the shore, wondering if anyone else on the beach had seen the man, but there was nobody else. He realised how far out he was. He had wandered off course, carried by the drifting sands, fixated on reaching the head of the estuary. It would be a short dash to the edge of the channel and then a longer run back to the safety of the beach. He could do it though. He had to be sure. He had to do what was right.

He set out at a jog, his boots slopping in the soft sand, the glasses banging against his chest. He wasn't a runner. Coming to the estuary was all the exercise he got, the walks around sands and marshes a break from the sedentary day-to-day of suburban commuting. Sally was content with the semi in Aldershot, and all the clubs and societies she kept herself busy with, the Women's Institute and the Girl Guides, the sports centre for gym, but it was nothing he'd ever felt able to share with her. Perhaps if the fertility treatment had worked out – but neither of them could face that again, all the anticipation and grief. At the weekends he had found himself walking the reservoirs and gravel pits where birds would stop off on their exhausting migrations. He felt an affinity. Every long journey needed a rest point, a break, and his was to be found by the water, with the birds, and he soon learned their names and calls, their distinct movements, losing himself in the migratory masses. Sally didn't mind the trips to the estuary. She almost seemed to welcome them. Three times a year he would drive up the M11 and grow lighter with every mile.

He slowed to a walk, his sides aching. It didn't help that the sand was sinking beneath him, the water rising up over his feet as the tide came in. He was wading like a sandpiper. The light glistered off the waves. He was in the channel, the sea already around him. As he looked over at the bulk of the old freighter, he thought of how in the First World War the ships were painted black and white, like the oystercatcher, to trick the eye. He waded deeper into the channel, felt the tug of the water coursing in around his calves. He thought he saw it again, something rolling in the currents and then gone. He splashed towards it.

Everything went black for a moment, and then he surfaced with a gasp. Saltwater slapped against his face. He'd have to swim for it now, get back to shore and call the coastguard. His camera bag was lost. His phone too then. He thought of how he'd tell it to Judith. It felt like the sort of thing that might bring them closer though, they'd laugh about it, and then it would make things all the more difficult. He would mend things with Sally, explain how all the years of hope and loss were a journey for him, and that he couldn't go back now to the way things were without a change, a sense of arrival.

He was treading water, trying to lose his welly boots with each kick. He thought he must have slipped off the edge of a bank into a deeper channel, the shallower water would be nearby. He had never been a strong swimmer, but he could hold his own in a pool for a few lengths. If there was anyone else in the sea they'd have to make it on their own. He realised with a cold jolt, it was him in the sea. It was only ever him. The same way he found himself, felt himself, in the wheeling flocks, he'd sensed himself in the channel and had followed the mirage like a fool. Judith would be looking out for him. Judith would see. She would be waiting for him with a towel and a cup of cocoa when he got back to the cottage.

He managed to free his feet and writhe out of his jacket. The binoculars still hung uselessly around his neck. He pulled them off and let them go, nearly going under as he did, then he took a few strokes towards the point he thought he'd slipped and a few more to be sure. He let his feet sink, feeling for the bottom, but they met nothing but the rocking, coursing waters. The sunlight flared off every wavelet. A swell broke over the now submerged sandbar and the water grabbed at him. The tide was pulling him, he realised, away from the sands and towards the head of the estuary. He kicked against it, trying to crawl back towards the beach. If he could get back he could explain things, put it right. Sally would have so many questions, and Judith wouldn't know the right answers to give. That girl hardly knew him.

The sea clutched his wet clothes, constraining him, as if in a fevered tangle of sheets. The muscles in his shoulders began to ache. He came gasping out of the crawl and trod water again, seeing the beach further away this time. There was a man on the shore, walking. Lucian tried to raise a hand, called out. The water swelled and he went under and up again, coughing water, struggling to locate the figure on the sands. He called out again, louder. He thought he saw a figure stop, break into a run, hit the water and wade in towards him, and then the vision faded, undid itself in the slap and dazzle of the sea. Lucian felt the current lock his legs and drag him, it flexed and flowed around him, muscular and swift. He was dissolving into the sea, into its skittering jabs of light.

He kicked again towards the shore, but he felt his legs fading. It didn't matter. Sally would understand. Sally would forgive him, with all they'd been through. Judith would be calling the coastguard. She'd be watching. He'd be pulled towards the mouth of the estuary and then pushed out again to sea. His hands grew numb. He could only tread water, struggle to keep his head up. He gasped, kicked, gasped, kicked. He could sense them, the redshanks and curlews, sandpipers and turnstones, as they took to the wing. He was losing himself in the great cloud of gathering oystercatchers, soaring and turning in their musical clamour, skirling in the last of the daylight. His body loosened. His legs were gone and so were his arms, and then his body and face as well, until there was nothing left but the sound and sight of rising birds.

Three Poems
Lane Ashfeldt

Irish Linen

Pure Irish Linen
a phrase from long ago
woven into those plain tea-towels
that smoothed away wet suds
from mother's wedding set.

Her good linen cloths
were kept to buff glass and china
or left safely in the drawer
while gaudier prints bore the grime
and stains of daily wear.

I teased her for it then,
not knowing the grown-up equation
of good with expensive.
And you didn't buy Pure Irish Linen,
it was a thing you were given.

A cloth spun and woven
from flax pulled and scutched
across the border, a fact on which
we did not dwell much, in Dublin,
where we never called it Ulster linen.

The words Pure, Irish, and Linen
no longer form an automatic cluster.
Instead we buy the best fabrics we can muster
regardless of origin,
whilst a machine blows our dishes dry.

Revolution Dot Com

On Moore Street they're selling black teeshirts
bearing the faces of the 1916ers
like some heavy metal band that rolled on for a century.
They've taken over the Rotunda.
Again.
Get past the guns and Kilmainham,
and you'll find the Hunger Strikers beneath the domed ceiling,
all sideburns and flowery shirts like a string of Seventies pop
stars.
Gone, but not forgotten.
Remembered every so often at least
in between all the other stuff
we've to keep up on,
our health and gourmet-conscious doctrines,
in between sessions at the gym
and quick posts on social media,
we who came into the land easy.
So here's another take-home slice of Ireland
to add to the Clonakilty black pudding
and the Cashel Blue,
to the replica Celtic Cross
that hangs on the wall:
the 'Michael Collins' Foxford rug.

∞

A tricolour picnic blanket

for the back of your beemer.
They say it washes very well.
Red wine and all sorts
rinse out of its natural fibres.
And isn't that a good thing
considering how messy that particular
summer's day spin was to get?
August 1922, in the one county you were sure
you'd be safe in. But twenty miles is a long way
from Shanakiel when your brain is slowly
spilling, the car rug soaking up your
dreams, your memories, your future.
You have kept Kitty waiting
one time too many.
This is it now
          the land you fought to stand on
      sucked out from under
the horizon on a heavy slant.
They did a good job these Cork soldiers
you trained them well. Brought the ground
up close to greet you, then slipped away

100 Revolutions Per Second

Had you known, then

that the wedding was to be off
and your name gifted to Kitty's second son
when she found a new man

that signed shadows of yourself in uniform
would feature on wove labels, to be sewn
on replicas of the tricolour throw
that draped your body

that this heavyweight woollen travel rug
the original a get-round for a soon to be legal flag
would grace our comfy sofas as a talking point
a century down the line

Would it have changed anything,
Would you still count the deal worth it,
Would it have stopped the wheel turning,

                    had you known?

Bánh ga to
John Saul

Another great frond swept imperiously by; palm or
banana, turned grey by the night. The leaves loomed,
approaching and vanishing, like blades revolving on a
giant fan. Then fog, the grey fog of an autumn night.
There might be fields, possibly water beside the track.
The train swayed and swung, banging and thumping
from unseeable causes.

To the other side of the little table with its blurs –
ghost versions of plastic water bottles and artificial
flowers, faint papers that would include the itinerary,
tickets, the familiar guidebook – Sarah stirred in her
bunk, shifting her weight to see out of the window, only
to jerk back as a monstrous leaf dipped by. People tell her
she reminds them of Helen Mirren. But in the grey her
face was any face. There were no shadows, no clear lines.
She blew her nose on a tissue. The tissue was a great
moth as it darted up and down, then vanished. In the
bunk above, Geert was a sack turned to the wall.

Sarah peered as I had into the all-transforming
pearly cloud. She was sure we were on top of a dyke. All
this jolting and clanking, she said, I'm scared. Of what?
Scared of death by water. Sarah feared the train would

tumble from the dyke. She described it in detail, in a babble. As the derailed carriage slung us through the air our stomachs would turn hollow. We would drown in shallows, far from home, our faces against stalks of rice.

Having travelled the route before, doubting such a fate, I said nothing. I hardly cared. I had Ali on my mind. Ali short for Alison. Wearing red, wearing green. I thought she was long forgotten. But there she was, her name, half her name, surfacing in the night. Geert turned over. Could Ali count as a case of unrequited love? I had no idea. Geert? Geert, are you scared too? said Sarah, say no or I'll get double scared. No response. Oh well, said Sarah. In the dark I heard her take a swig of water, screw back the top and knock at the bunk above. Want some Geert? No reply.

We would arrive before dawn. Sarah switched on the lamp by her head, to look at the Guide. Bending the familiar red spine, leafing back and forth, she swore the maps shifted onto different pages each time she looked. Since yesterday, she insisted a new section on food had appeared. Photos of a lantern shop and the water-puppet theatre had exchanged places. Geert must have heard for he said above the banging of the carriage: we are the only still points. I glanced at him fingering the beads on his necklace. The very travel plans move, said Sarah. Travel plans were a sore point for her, literally. She had walked miles with a bad knee, miles that were not in the plans. On the tour bus she told the driver: have us walk an extra step and I'll sit on your head.

Sarah bossed. She had been sending Geert on missions and awaiting his reports. Ambivalent about the Q, the hotel that acts as the base for the tour, she detailed him to investigate alternative accommodation. I showed him one hotel. We checked out the dining room. There was Ho Chi Minh, sampling pancakes and slices of pineapple. This Ho Chi Minh had the right height and bearing for an Uncle Ho, the same long grey beard arrangement, same gaunt face. He had the peace, the quiet confidence; and at his table several newspapers (Ho was a voracious reader), lying ready for him to work his way through over juice and cereal. There are many Ho Chi Minhs, Geert reckoned, much as there are many Elvises. This Uncle Ho was American, it turned out, one of the few in evidence hereabouts.

Sleep Sarah sleep, said Geert turning back to the wall. Outside a light shone in the mist. A lantern, a boat? A branch rapped along the window; another palm waved by, huge, as if it were the national flag. I tried out the idea on myself: the national flag, unofficial, was a banana leaf. I was unconvinced; it would never fly from any pole. More grey night. I kept silent. When talking to people on their tours I take care to conceal my purpose: I helped create the Guide and am now checking this and that detail, such as the alternatives to the night train arriving at an awkward time, or the going price for a rickshaw, or complaints that the hotel reception back in Lao Cai is dominated by a dragon.

The dragon wore the puffy headdress of a Red Dao woman, red *zao*. To me the dragon was charming. She sorted a problem over damp table salt as if it was the best thing that could have befallen us. I have to say she was overly possessive of the hotel umbrellas. I swear to you, she told me, their number each day drops sharply then around mid-afternoon it rises; as if they go and come back by themselves. Umbrellas, maps, trains. All on the move. The country is swaying. Trains and boats and planes. Then there are the mopeds: almost one hundred per cent motorbike ownership according to the *Saigon Times* (Kawasaki, Suzuki, Yamaha; Honda are currently the most popular).

Get a Honda Dream II or Super Dream, I recalled hearing the words of the director of the Q, who is a collector. Mr Huỳnh habitually sits cross-legged on a bench tucked inside the door to the street. His own machines, grey smoky *cyclos*, their long bodies and soft, ancient tyres, line the hallway. He says he has a Minsk which still runs perfectly (but where was it? – he wouldn't say). Mr Huỳnh is also a master architect, which accords him much respect. He is expected to say the wisest thing. I looked forward to Mr Huỳnh, to breakfast, though not breakfast at the Q. The Q is for rest, for later. Then I might try the black Yamaha piano. Or the roof garden with its orchids and Buddha. I could lean on the parapet and see those two ornamental dragons, as they ripple along a roof ridge in grey stone.

Meanwhile I know where to go for that breakfast: for *bánh ga to*, a plain confection, with mango slices and coffee. I see the *ga to* before me, a clear sign of hunger. I see the cup waiting beside it. The tin strainer steams; hot water seeps onto the condensed milk and sugar. Chicory makes the coffee bitter, turning it into a national phenomenon; sweet and bitter, sugar and chicory, yin to yang. The *ga to* – it's explained – quietly soaks up these contradictions. It has to do something of the sort; the ready drink tastes of incense, jasmine and diesel fumes; roast meat, hints of hemp, currant, marijuana. The mother of Mr Huỳnh, who sits outside the Q – a grandmother – says the coffee has too much earth, too much blood. But in sipping it the granddaughter says she can connect to another place, where there are dragonflies and buffalo and white rice birds flying back and forth. The dragonflies that have touched the coffee plant have hovered by buffalo grazing, and settled on lotus leaves nodding in their pools.

A broad blade looms, slaps against the glass and vanishes. Flicking open another tissue, another moth, Sarah turns away. She complained earlier of not feeling herself, and was also anxious to rest her knee, which caused her to miss the long walk through the rice fields. In the fields was another Red Dao woman. Her name was My~. I wrote about the Dao in the Guide. I described how they, like the Black Hmong, assign one woman to each Westerner walking. The women simply materialise, as if dropping from the trees – in no time it is as if they have always been there, with you. They are extremely sociable. First comes talk, a morning long. They are more than ready to lend a rough, strong, country hand when crossing streams, or negotiating mud or stony paths. Business is arrived at later, with trinkets and handmade clothes. Look down at the new scarf, the new purse, then look up. The moment sales have been concluded – they've vanished.

My~ was small and brown and slender, her smile a glory. She talked (as often the way with the Dao) as if we had met by coincidence; she had just taken her young children to school. As we walked the path between the fields a thick mist fell, then lifted. I know you, she said before taking a drink from a bottle. She showed me a strip of red cloth. She smiled. This is for you, she said. She would hang it from a tree. *Whoa!* says Sarah at a heavy lurch; a new clanking starts. Did My~ do that, hang it from a tree, and when was that? The carriage feels on a bend. I peer out of the window, half expecting to see this cloth hanging as we pass; wishing to see it. Instead there's an assortment of dwellings the same grey as the leaves. We are approaching the city proper. First the track enters like a tramline, close to the houses. In Hanoi the streets will look covered in dust. The odd scattered lights make them look that way; but they are; they are covered in dust.

Suddenly Geert dangles an arm towards Sarah. You asleep Sarah, I can't believe we saw China: pass the water. Sarah reaches up a bottle. Did we really? she replies, because I don't know about you but I saw the hills across the river, then the river was gone, the hills gone. Yeah, agrees Geert with a burp, excuse me – gone. Disappeared utterly, he amplifies, but there you are: nothing is permanent. I shut out what Geert has to say, and instead remember stopping to watch the winnowing of rice, halfway up a hill, at a spot apparently relied on for the breeze. Do you know me? said My~. Curiously, I did, somehow. I think I recognise you from somewhere, I said, have you been to Hanoi, surely not? My~ smiled; she hitched her basket up on her slight shoulders. Yeah yeah yeah, Geert is saying. Sarah flicks the pages of the Guide rapidly back and forth. They really do, she says to him, the maps in the book move; like when you shake a kaleidoscope. But Geert is back facing the wall.

Do they move? The national motto, unofficial, is to keep moving. Mopeds, trains, everything. China, umbrellas. Ho Chi Minh, lotus leaves in their pools. At the temple of literature stone tortoises have disappeared. I lie back, thinking to test the whole idea carefully: is everything on the move, shifting, name something that isn't moving. Take something big, really big, how about the National Assembly, well yes and no, it was *about* to move, to a new home, on the city outskirts. But it didn't. Scatterings of soil by geomancers divined great trouble. Their objections to the site stopped it moving. Geomancers. What they would make of the Q.

Lights shine next to the train, moving in and out of the fog. Two buffalo stand close, revealing brown hides and black eyes, and vanish. The grey has gained something, what is it, moonlight, smoke. It's the colour of the dust in the streets. More lights, muffled shouts, engines. There are the roadways in the dust, motorbikes waiting at the crossing gates. We are arriving. We've stopped. More urgent shouts. *Cyclos* on the platform, where already passengers are milling. Policemen consulting clipboards. Geert clambers down, scrambling to find his shoes. Into the tumult, says Sarah with her rucksack. Absurdly, I look around for Ali, for dark curls in all the heads, curls that are doubtless thousands of miles from here. We join the discharging trainload of passengers; now it's us who are moving. Adjusting to the necessary pace we flow together without a choice, like water down a river, to flop into the station hall. I help Sarah and Geert negotiate a taxi to the Q; we separate and wave, leaving me to head down the street of mats and rugs, the street selling shoes, turn into *Hang Chieu*, down *Dinh Liet*, cross the avenue by the lake.

Having negotiated the last roadway I slow to a stroll, stopping often. There's a faint green to the dawn. By the lake lights are draped about the trees. The strips of grass are filled by people performing exercises. Alongside whirls the *cyclo* traffic, another relentless, swirling river. I watch, following movements and trying to memorise one or two which seem more elegant. I look at the lake for its famous old turtle which you would be lucky to see once in a lifetime, I forget its name, before indulging in the coffee and cake, and mango. As the only customer, I have a table above the water. The situation calls for romance. I look around for some. It would be fine if the rising sun were mango-coloured, but the sky – the orange – isn't clean enough. Right below a Ho Chi Minh holds the boat painter as a couple climb excitedly into a pedal boat. They almost disappear in mist and haze.

Why not join us for breakfast? Sarah had said. Why not. I should have. As the only one at the tables I'm at a loose end. A loose end from what? A love affair, what love affair? The coffee has an aftertaste of herbs. The *ga to* sweeps them up. The mango happily pursues the cake. Across the water the pedal boat drifts, as the couple get absorbed with their mobile phones. Squealing, they pedal back frantically. They phone, they pedal; phone, pedal; the pattern repeats itself. Meanwhile the haze persists. I pay.

On the walk to the Q the haze, like cloud off an ocean, still shrouds the tops of buildings. The most direct route passes the puppet theatre, leads down the street with children's clothes, past the hairdressers, before reaching the street of shops – this is sounding like the Guide itself – arraying fake and real silver, and dotted with hotels like the Q.

Mr Huỳnh is sitting cross-legged by the doors. Sarah is leaning her head on an arm, on the reception desk. It has emerged she has a temperature, put down to fried fish eaten yesterday – fucking fish, *tuna* in a fucking *banana* leaf, she says with her head still on her arm,

served at a table in the dark. Everything, she says
straightening up, *every*thing has gone stupid. Today
someone had already told her she reminded them of
Helen Mirren. She'll have to gain a few pounds, she's
saying, meaning Helen Mirren would have to, to look
like her. Next thing we're in and out of the lift and she's
waving me into their hotel room, asking what's keeping
Geert on his errand. He's been detailed to find silk at
under eight dollars a metre. The room is dark with
teakwood. You know what, Sarah says, if I don't feel
better by tonight I will give the water puppets a miss, yes
yes, Geert will bring photos, but have I come seven
thousand miles to look at a couple of photos from a hotel
bed, *no*. Bent over, she lurches to the bathroom and in the
same moment starts retching. The room has a kettle. I
switch it on. I sit on the end of the bed, the only place not
piled with things. More retching. The revolving fan on
the ceiling clicks round.

Sarah emerges and brushes clothes onto the floor
in order to clamber into bed, where she occupies the very
centre, sitting up, an apparition, very pale against the
headboard. I suggest tea, weak tea and I could go and
find some *ga to*. Sarah's voice is quiet: all right, tea; as
long as it isn't that godawful coffee. The water boils. I'll
make the pagoda tomorrow, she says talking to the
ceiling and watching the fan. If anybody up there tries to
stop me, I'll sit on their head. I make the tea and hand it
to her. She wants to know things – as a kind of
compensation for not going out, for not seeing the

puppets. I'd been here before hadn't I, had I seen the puppets? How did they manipulate them, was it from behind a curtain? Is it true they had poles attached? And what is this *ga to*?

Speaking like the co-author of the Guide I take her copy from the bedside and recite: to make a *ga to*, you need 4 *quả trứng gà*, 100 grammes—Sarah snatches the book and tries the words, before half-heartedly lobbing a pillow down the bed. '*Ga to*, the national cake in your mixing bowl,' she quotes. What is this, and where *is* there some? – not that I want any; and anyway there's no such thing as national cake. Maybe there is, unofficially, I say; feeling any better now? No, she says, but thanks.

This was my opportunity to get out of there. I went up to the roof garden. It had rained in the night. The Buddha gazed. The ornamental dragons snarled their inward snarls. The Buddha said neither stay nor go. I went. Back on the landing, through a doorway, the Yamaha stood unplayed. But the thought of playing would be a further reminder: I was at a loose end. Did she call herself Ali, or was it just other people called her that? – I hardly knew her. I was, I had been falling in love. But was too slow, or too clumsy. She went for *him*. We never met. He was just *him*. She and he seemed to sail away, out of reach. They just: floated away. Vanished. Could the result be this feeling, habit – of too easily being at a loose end? Of breakfasting alone; daydreaming over playing some neglected piano; looking out of the window at night?

What to do? I go and joke with the hotel staff, who are arguing how best to look after some paper lotus flowers a guest has bought: should they be laid flat or kept upright? I have to stroll away; I've no idea. By the door Mr Huỳnh is not talking to anyone, not even reading some magazine; he's just *there*. I ask if he likes coffee. He smiles. In the air there's a faint suspicion he knows, only he, of my connection to the Guide. He does like coffee, very much. He nods towards the chatter: Over flowers made of paper, he says with a laugh, but here we are paper lovers – have you noticed we have only paper money in our country, we have no coins, and doesn't it make things easier? This fails to fit inside my head, which is full of the love affair that never was, the Dao arranging people's spirits about the trees; the recipe for *ga to*, the great leaves in the night, rice drifting in the air; a picture of Sarah in bed sitting up, indeed looking faintly like Helen Mirren. I retire to the Yamaha and try a few scraps of tunes, badly; no national anthems, unofficial or otherwise, nothing meaningful.

A night's sleep has been lost. The bench beside the piano is spread with cushions. I lie on it and dream about the puppet theatre. There were bright-faced puppets of fishermen and farmers and buffalo and birds. Nervously on the move, men fought with men and scrapped with women, fish swam circles and ducks climbed trees. In a box by the stage a six-strong orchestra accompanied the cavorting. On and on went the laughing, the wailing and the drowning – even in the middle of this dream came a revelation, the significance of the water dawning, this was the water wherever rice was grown, or lotus grew – the splashing this way and that, forever moving, the non-stop action, the pursuing and fleeing from explosions, tigers, fires and flying dragons. For the entire performance one musician, big dark buttons down the centre of her grey silk gown, had her head bowed to the instrument on her lap. Amid the frantic scrambling, struggling and rejoicing, she was plucking and plucking demurely. Not until the curtain call did she look up, and the face was familiar. Her face? Was it her face? Was she moving here and there, like the city plans, the tortoises, umbrellas? I knew her from somewhere. It was her. She floated off with him, as if to a sort of underworld, and later accompanied me about the rice fields.

On the Mattress
Lander Hawes

Today I am a tourist who is tired because his delayed flight was cancelled, and yesterday I was a divorced taxi driver who hadn't spoken to his son for a year, but the subject I am following is the same. He's wearing his blue-checked shirt, the one from the department store sale, and he's in the cafe where he usually drinks his milky morning coffee. It's the wide-fronted cafe near the Museum; the one with the shutter whose opening and closing is notably loud: a shrill and metallic ascent or descent, a scrape and abbreviated shriek.

I am unshaven in another cafe across the square in my crumpled suit and glasses with unmodified lenses. The luggage pulled close to my chair contains two disguises and my daughter's flamethrower. I glimpse the subject now and again between the pedestrians, and I am watching him on my phone via the cafe security cameras. My superiors are concerned that he is communicating in code with the radical faction; they believe that the subject has a system of wearing particular colours in particular places at particular times. These superiors are interested in the street signs that he stands beneath, and whether he is wearing or holding his hat as he stands under each one, and if he's holding the hat whether it's in his right or left hand.

A pretty waitress asks him a question, and he smiles and asks a question back. Her surprised laugh, and the way a slant of light illuminates his handsome face, the playful tilt in the line of his mouth, the warmth of the humour in his expressive eyes, makes me wish that I was seated at his table, smiling in the collaborative way that a friend might. Only his ordinary desires are concealed when he looks, and even these are hidden in a way that offers their concealing as a compliment. \

I lay the phone down and consider risking a toilet visit. The milky froth is still topping his coffee, but the demands and responsibilities of his position often interrupt this morning drink: sometimes he leaves a cup part-drunk, usually after receiving a call from his party's public relations official and so has to attend an unscheduled meeting or resolve some problem at his office. I decide to chance it and hurry to the door, hauling my luggage behind. In the cubicle the phone buzzes: it's a call which I'm professionally obliged to answer.

'Hello Bargis.'

'It's Victud.'

'Hello Victud.'

'Where are you?'

'In the toilet in the cafe on the north side of Mektebi square.'

The stupid music that Victud and Bargis have on in their van, the kind that's played all day on building sites and all night in jails, is so loud I can barely hear him.

'Is anything happening?'

I am tempted to make an ironic reply about my bowel but I refrain because Victud and Bargis are too psychopathic to have the kind of sense of humour that most citizens would recognise as a sense of humour.

'The usual morning. He is drinking coffee at one table. So am I at another.'

'You need to come with us. We'll collect you in five minutes. Be on the street at the front.'

'What have you done?'

'Be on the street.'

Victud and Bargis are the enforcers for this sub-district, and undoubtedly monitor me for our superiors. When they arrive I'm glad to see that the passenger seat has been fitted across the width of the van; I lift the luggage in and shove it along the seat and climb up and slide the door closed. Also, they've attached a curtain behind the passenger seat, most likely torn from a rail in a dissident's bedroom, to hide the mattress in the back.

I imagine the mattress is still there though, down on the floor, and I can't express how relieved I am that I haven't had to walk over it, or even, heaven forbid, sit on the mattress as they drive erratically along the streets, mounting pavements and pushing between vehicles at junctions on red lights, all the while laughing and spitting out of the windows and calling to passing girls and women. The mattress is heavily stained: when they found it in a derelict hotel the fabric was already ringed with dried circles of human fluids in discarded-bandage yellow and amputation-discharge brown. Each time I see Victud and Bargis the mattress has new hues and crusts and overlays of stains: it is the only honest record. Their attitude is that the suspects, the internees, the detained should be thankful; for the two of them, the mattress represents a concession.

'Where are we going?'

'East.'

'Shouldn't we put a bag over his head, Bargis?'

'Why Victud, why should we do that? We can trust him, can't we?'

'Yes, but he's so ugly.'

Victud's laughing makes his shoulders jolt up and down, as if he is driving over broken ground or throttling someone who is strong enough to resist.

Bargis part turns, so his face is in profile.

'We have a little mission, a little task for you.'

'I want to tell him, Bargis.'

'No, Victud. It's my turn. You always get the fun job.'

'Okay but you buy the ice creams instead.'

Bargis turns further to look at me; his hand dangles from the seat edge and his elbow swivels to point at my stomach.

'Open the curtain.'

'I don't want to Bargis.'

'No, have a look.'

The shape of Bargis's horrible thin lips is stirring towards a horrible thin smile; it's clear he's beginning to enjoy himself and that his interest is piqued. I really don't want to see or hear Bargis laugh; it is the mocking laugh of a man whose essential habitat is a dungeon, a man who needs dungeons in the way that others need libraries or casinos or cafes.

'Have you got a plastic bag?'

'You won't vomit. Not this time. It's not like that.'

I slide the curtain. The corpse of a little old lady is lying on the mattress. Her swollen ankles within the loose folds of her pale tights make her black shoes seem tiny. Mercifully, she is fully clothed. Her face, already sallow and brown-tinged beneath the eyes, has the settled flesh of a ministered death.

'She looks very nice, doesn't she?'

'How did she go?'

I'd wanted to ask how she was murdered, but they'd notice.

'Guess?'

'Heart? I can't see any, uh, interference.'

'She smells lovely,' Victud says. 'I like the old lady smell, you know, dried flowers or herbs.'

Bargis holds up an oxygen mask with attached transparent tubing. Leaning forward, I see a two-cylinder backpack in his footwell.

'Poison gas. It's the newest thing. Cheaper than bullets.'

'Why her?'

'We were in a big hurry.' Victud says. 'She was leaving the target's house; the target was an old lady. You know.'

'They look alike, the old ladies,' Bargis says.

'So your target was a grandmother?'

'Yes yes.'

'There's a whole new system. No more of this waiting and watching and taking. No more questions at the end. Now the subjects just have to go. We have this weekly quota.'

Bargis flourishes a piece of paper.

'There are all these names.'

'We're here,' Victud says. He brakes hard and I jolt forward so fast that the seat belt locks. Bargis almost drops the piece of paper, denying me the chance to pick it up and glance at the list whilst handing it back. Behind, the mattress shifts and rasps and I remember that before the ascendance of the regime Victud delivered pizzas.

After a few minutes of Victud's enthusiastic instructions and cramped, unnecessary demonstrations I find myself at the rear of a small house holding her calves while Victud has his elbows under the armpits and his hands clasped on the chest; her head is tipped forward, yawing and lolling as if she was unconscious in a collapsed hammock.

'Don't you have a stretcher?'

'Bargis snapped it attacking a doctor.'

The slip of paper is in his shirt pocket and I'm preventing myself glancing there; the visible printed text is almost readable.

'You'll be with us for the next few weeks.'

'I see.'

'What flavour ice cream do you like?'

The radio on Victud's belt buzzes twice: the agreed signal for us to enter.

'Go on.'

I nudge the unlocked door with my back and shuffle into a kitchen. As we move towards the kitchen doorway Bargis's voice becomes audible from the front room.

'So you say you last saw her this morning. What time exactly was that?'

There's a muffled reply, and then Victud is hissing.

'Turn, turn. Your left.'

We circle around into a hallway.

'The stairs.'

Loud thumps are coming from the front room, and the crash of shattering glass.

'You first.'

I back tentatively up. The stairs are narrow, and I fumble with a heel for the edge of each step. As we climb the angle of the old lady inclines from ninety degrees to closer to one hundred and twenty. The hem of her skirt slips back towards her waist.

The kitchen door bangs open.

'They're Christians,' Bargis shouts through.

'What?' Victud replies.

Bargis is approaching the threshold of the kitchen and the hallway. He is dragging an old man by gripping both ankles, sliding him across the tiles of the kitchen to the polished wooden floor of the hall.

'They're fucking Christians,' he says.

'You're joking.'

Victud half-turns towards Bargis.

'No really.'

Victud releases the old lady. As she drops his hands run up the lengths of her arms, as if she has flung them up in a gesture.

'Let her go.'

I don't move.

'The legs you idiot.'

By now her head is resting against his knees and I see my chance and let go so that she piles against his shins and he has to split his legs and grab a banister to avoid being toppled. I step down as if to assist and grasp his outstretched arm and step close and manage to pincer the list in his breast pocket between two fingers whilst seizing his shirt front. Meanwhile, she tumbles and slides, her head and heels making horrible, hollow collision noises on the steps and the banisters.

'Whoopee,' Bargis cries.

He is swivelling the old man at his waist, still clutching the ankles and building momentum by pivoting, in the gleeful manner of a father playing with a child. He rotates in the width of the hallway, aided by the weight of the canisters on his back, before launching the old man towards the stair base. The head comes to rest by his wife's, whose legs are on the steps, with her outstretched arms and head on the floor, twisted and facing up.

Victud stands on the old man's chest as he hastens over the bodies.

'Let's make a coffee.'

'Christians. Yes,' Bargis shouts at me before following Victud into the kitchen. I step over the couple, hoping to recall some religious phrase to whisper. I wonder if alive they'd ever lain this way: their bodies apart but heads tucked together; perhaps when swimming, adrift and swayed by a swell, in the shallows of a summer ocean, eyelids closed as if counting for a game.

The unfolded list is in my palm, and sure enough the name of my subject, the man I have been following, is near the top of the column.

'You want a coffee?'

Victud is in the kitchen doorway.

'No. I had one in the cafe.'

'What's that?'

'It's this. It fell out of your pocket on the stairs.'

'Oh. Thank you.'

I follow him in. Bargis is piling cutlery into the microwave.

'Should I polish it?'

'No there's no need,' Victud replies.

'We should do it with the candles and the gas as well.'

'You see any candles?'

'There must be some.'

'Why?'

'Because they're Christians.'

Both men start laughing. On the fridge there are photographs of children and grandchildren I'm trying not to look at.

'Hey,' Bargis says to me. 'I just remembered. Do you still have the flamethrower? The prize from the school?'

Victud looks between us. I want to lie but I daren't; they will check the luggage.

'I don't think there's any gas left.'

'Go get it.'

Victud stares at Bargis.

'You mean you're going to let him do it?'

Bargis leans his head to one side, as if mimicking speaking to a child.

'Don't worry Victud. I still like you. He'll be doing this a lot from now. We all need to start somewhere.'

'Can I burn the corpses if he burns the house?'

'I want him to burn the corpses, Victud.'

*

Today I am the leader of a popular political movement who is about to signal in code to the radical faction but who does not know that he has been followed every day for two months. I am standing on the other side of the street from my subject who has just arrived to stand beneath the street sign there. He is wearing a blue-checked shirt and black jeans and brown shoes and so am I and my hair is styled and tinted to resemble his. We are both carrying folded caps in our left hands. On noticing me he stares and frowns and I stare back and then I make a gun shape with two straight fingers and a curved thumb and prod my hair hard enough to rupture the pouch of fake blood taped to my scalp and I drop to my knees with the red liquid streaming as if pretending to die on a stage. I'm hoping I won't have to repeat myself to him and also that Victud and Bargis won't phone too soon.

Three Poems
Ellen Davies

Photo from the fair

You place a candy striped towel
on the seat beneath my bare legs
to protect them from the hot metal.
I choose the blue squirrel, shunning
the orange dog. One of my bunches
has worked loose, sun-lightened hair
gathering in the collar of my denim jacket.
I'm holding the handles tightly, primed,
preparing for the ride to start,
the slow merry-go-round,
that will turn me, inevitably,
out of your sight.

Smoking Cigars

I was drunk, twenty-one,
when I first tasted a cigar.
I'd never smoked before,
apart from that time, aged twelve
when I secreted a drag
from the scrap of a fag
in the back lane. That time,
I choked, red,
thought I'd never catch
my breath again,
but the cigar
was different, its brown neck
smooth between my fingers,
the familiar hint of vanilla and spice
released by the flick of a lighter.
Drawing in the smoke, I tasted
summer, Spanish holidays
in September, your Hamlets
carried on sea air.

Cupping the memory between lips,
I held my breath, afraid to breathe
the last essence of you out.

Strongbow

It had been in the fridge
for over a year,
the solitary can of cider
you never had the chance
to drink.

On your birthday,
we poured it out
under the tree
where we lay
part of you to rest
and watched
thirsty roots
drink you in.

Visiting the same spot
a week later I'm sure
the tree has grown greener:
the cut roses
we covered you with
still hold their colour,
fed strong on your stubborn
ash and cider.

And Three Things Bumped
Kelly Creighton

I think of Stephen Kent and I remember the first time he
ever collected me in that taxi of his. His name and
number on a laminated card swinging on the rear-view
mirror. You know the type of thing I'm talking about. He
told me a fill from the moment I got into his car at the
airport pick up zone: Stephen had been a *transplant* in
Chelsea until he'd come back home where, all over the
province, he bought houses as investments, apart from
the one he was renovating for his family. Sitting good-
naturedly in Friday dinner time traffic, he'd boasted his
wife was living with her parents until the new homestead
was shipshape. Stephen used to work in stocks, making
money from money. Back then I toyed with writing:
making something from nothing or stories from stories. I
suppose there are more than two ways of looking at the
one thing.

Outside my home he said, That's a nice wee house
you have there.

Cheers, I said, about to leave.

Stephen said, This place is overrun with kids. How
many have you got yourself?

One, I told him, and one on the way.

He turned the radio off completely. I've three, he said, two lads and a girl. He sat back so he was looking at me full on in the rear-view mirror. He was somewhere between a pair of eyes and a hard thick neck. You have to give stuff up when kids are involved, don't you, Stephen said.

We only had our daughter then so I couldn't tell if that would catch us up. Trudy and I didn't stop each other doing the things we loved. I thought about her and her surfing, and me and my writing. Stephen and I got talking and lost track of time. Trudy looked out the living room window at us.

Someone wants you home, Stephen said though neither of us moved.

Trudy's easy-going, I told him.

That's good, he said. Then you're lucky man.

Stephen told me his neighbours were young guys. They invited him to the bar, coaxed him into going to Ravenhill to watch the rugby. Stephen normally ended up driving. He said sometimes he felt they used him for lifts. There was never any point in leaving the Merc at home, which was the car he drove when he wasn't taxiing, and he didn't charge them. They're not a bad crowd, he told me. It's good to have the company of young fellas.

Stephen had a decade on me. Just had his fortieth. He had a thing for numbers which I understood as being residual from his broker days. He talked about being born on the tenth of May, that his daughter had the same birthday. He was one of ten kids.

I think ten might be my lucky number, he said.

I listened quite easily. Always thirsty for a story back then. He elaborated on his living arrangements, admitting he and his wife were on a trial separation he believed they'd reconcile from, especially once she saw this house he was building for her and the children: whom I recall were seven and nine and ten, or thereabouts.

I said, Forgive my nosiness but is there anyone else in the picture?

No, none of that, Stephen told me. He was still wearing his wedding ring. I'll tell you something, he said, and it goes no further. In my experience money is the killer. People can put up with all sorts. Cheating would never do the damage money does.

So let me get this straight, I said, it's having too much money that ruins things?

He squinted in the mirror at me. Money is the killer, he repeated. It always has been with me and the missus. She wanted me to come back here so she could be near the grandparents for babysitting. She said she was lonely in Chelsea. All those millions of people and she couldn't find one she liked! We used to holiday in Dubai. New York. You sacrifice things, don't you? The house you want, the motors. I came back for her and what happened? If I'm being honest – and what's the point in not being – she was a very selfish person. What she put me through – and I'll not get into it all – but there aren't many men who would put up with the things that I put up with. In the end I couldn't any more.

Yes, you can't be doing with that, I said.

He dried up, so I told him it had been good talking to him. Stephen turned side on and shook my hand. He liked the look of the cufflinks Trudy had bought me: two silver crowns with little jewels set into the spikes. They were flash for my taste. A gift for my thirtieth I didn't have long. I lost one in the airport after a month or two. Trudy never really forgave me. One is, after all, sort of jobless on its own.

Stephen knew they were Westwood, who, as it turned out, was the only designer Stephen wore when he lived in Chelsea. Then out of nowhere he said, My wife did time. You asked so I'm going to tell you. She did time for fraud. Was stealing from me the whole time, and from her employer.

Jesus, I said and sat back, what else could I do?

Ruth, he said, that's her name. When Ruth came to Chelsea she got a job for the Crown Prosecution Service, started writing dodgy receipts. I just couldn't live with a woman like that, not in my profession. If you really want to know, I had to leave the market. I was warned it could have repercussions on me. They did me a severance deal and I took it. I'd be a tool not to. Ruth comes from a family…well, let's just say they aren't short of a bob or two, so between them and me the kids are kept right, you

know. And Ruth too. And I don't want you to think that I
wish her ill, because I don't.

No of course not, I said.

But if I wasn't a gentleman I could tell you a few
things, said Stephen.

How long did she do?

Where? Inside? Not long. He rubbed his eye. A
good solicitor, if you ever need one, is all you need.
Remember that, pal. If you ever find yourself on the
wrong side of the law, a shit-hot solicitor will seal the
deal. And keep your mouth shut. It does you no good if
you can't hold your water, do you know what I'm
saying?

I presume you get what you pay for, I said. In
terms of legal representation. Same as everything.

Absolutely, he nodded. It is the same as
everything. Especially in money issues. A good solicitor
will talk it all around and before you know it you don't
know what end of you is up. Well, Joe Bloggs doesn't
know. People who aren't used to money chat. It has its
own language. I don't need to be doing this, I live in a
real nice place, nice but small, I like working with people.
You couldn't beat it really. He yawned. Look, it's been
good talking to you but I have to get back now, the kids
will be calling me. I like to tell them I love them every
day. Even days I don't see them. Make sure you do that
too. Especially when the next one comes along, Stephen
added letting me know he had been listening. Don't let
the wee child feel left out. It's not a nice thing. I'm saying

this as the eldest of a large family. And you're on the right tracks too, going away to do your own thing, maybe me and Ruth should have done more of that. You get out of the way of it. Don't end up like us.

Okay, I said and we re-enacted our handshake.

They are nice cufflinks, he said, nearly longingly and he turned to put his hands back on the wheel.

They are quite nice, I said and I finally got out.

He was some talker, I said. Trudy shook her head and said she'd made something in the restaurant and there was plenty of it left in the fridge.

That night we lay in bed discussing Stephen. She was sceptical, like I had been, like anyone would be. Why would he be taxiing if he's so loaded, she asked.

He turned the meter off all that time we were sat outside.

I should hope so too.

He did say something good, that we should never stop doing the things we love.

Well then, Trudy said, maybe he was worth listening to.

*

We put ourselves aside for a couple of years. It happens, even though you vow it won't. Having a kid is a whirlwind. The house needed doing up. That fell by the wayside too. We slept together once, maybe twice a month, if we weren't exhausted. Having a second child was twice the work. It makes sense but somehow I hadn't bargained on it. At times it seemed we might crack.

We went to Paris for a weekend. Trudy's dad minded the kids. He hadn't a clue, poor man. Their clothes hadn't even been unpacked when we returned. God knows what he was doing. Potty training the youngest had to start all over again, but at least we got away. We had a good time but it felt cultural like a school trip. Our feet were worn to the bone with all the walking, then we fell asleep watching the show at the Moulin Rouge.

A week after we came home we spoke about it, how we should have been unable to keep our hands off each other, in Paris of all places. We wondered aloud if we were done. And what we would do with the house. How would we tell the kids? It happened in a blink.

I looked at Trudy and she looked at me and started crying, saying we were like passing ships. I'm so busy I'm meeting myself at the front door, she said. I'm going to miss you so much.

It struck me how ridiculous we were being, how easily we were prepared to tear our little family apart. I don't want this, I told her.

Nor do I, she said in a heavy wet voice. You're my favourite person in the world. All our friends always say we're perfect for each other and we are.

It was then Stephen came into my head, and everyone else I knew who had split up with their partners, especially where kids were involved, and I knew Trudy and I could hold it together. I told her she should go back to surfing and I should go back to writing. It would mean that our time together would be less but quality.

*

It must have been three years on, I was coming home from a writing retreat and Trudy had the car. She needed it because she was working nine to five. The kids were both at school by then and we had finally found a good design in the way we lived. We were at a good stage. The kids liked to learn and you could have conversations with them. And me and Trudy laughed together lots. It was then we were at our happiest, together and with the kids, but then I wondered, because we never *really* spoke, what was on her mind. We were like colleagues, in the many revolutions our relationship had taken. Although we were connected more in bed but it was all a bit predictable. Then once in a while we would have a mind-blowing night and my head would ease for another while.

I got a bit jealous of Trudy's new happiness, I have to admit. She was working in the prisons and I'd expected her to hate it, but she was getting something emotionally that we didn't seem to need from each other any more. I was working too, and writing, but it wasn't really going anywhere. I wasn't putting myself out there. Wasn't seeking publication. Something always held me back.

When Stephen collected me he asked about the retreat. I told him about the lake, how you walked around it for inspiration, how it was peaceful but I wanted to write strong stuff that really was the opposite of how it had been there.

But you did get peace and quiet to do it, he asked.

I did, I said.

His name card was stuck to the dash now and it had a photo. I could see his face but still his eyes flitted to me in the mirror. He was driving another heap of junk, working for a company instead of for himself. The radio kept coming through, telling him and his colleagues where to go next. Stephen lowered the volume.

I haven't seen you around in ages, I said to him.

He looked at me in the mirror. His hard thick neck tensed. I realised I wouldn't know him out on the street. You gave me a lift in the past, I said. You were going through some things back then.

Like what, he said.

You were maybe splitting up with your wife, pal, I said.

That's right, he said but Stephen was chary. How are you doing, pal?

Not bad, I said.

And what about this writing? Are you writing a book, he said.

I am, I said. Been writing it for years. I'm blocked.

Ah, he said. I have a story for you. You can have it if you want. It's about a woman who ended up in jail for stealing money from her employer and wrangled her way out of the conviction. You'll sell millions of copies.

He had no memory of me. Had probably told this story thousands of times since I'd last been in his cab. Instead of letting him think I'd spent all that time mulling it over, I pretended I'd never heard it. Is this a real story, I asked him.

It's real alright. It's my ex I'm talking about. She spent time inside, got the conviction turned over, came out and got it fixed on another poor fucker.

Jesus, that's mad, I said.

Are you married, he wanted to know first.

Practically. A very long term relationship, I said.

You'd never believe what they'd do to you. Honest to god, you just never know.

Sounds terrible.

I was living in London, he said. I met this girl on the net, Ruth, and I left there to be with her. She already had three kids. Two lads and one girl. All different dads: that should say it all! I came over here to be with her. She was cute. I'll give her that. Nice little shape to her. I talked her into moving back to London with me. We left the kids with her parents for a while to give things a go.

The plan was they were going to come over too. Listen to this for coincidence, her daughter's birthday was on the same day as mine. Tenth of May, he said. I'm one of ten kids and Ruth lived in 10 Gorse Lane. You know, you have to listen to all these signs when they're as powerful as that.

Absolutely you do!

I had my own business over there, a taxi firm – he had excluded the stockbroker line – and she was bored so I encouraged her to get out and work. We walked into a registry office one day and got married.

Weren't your family annoyed to have missed out?

Ah, no, I've been married before. They're not bothered. My mother never liked Ruth anyway.

Why not?

All the kids.

He pulled up into town. Fuck sake, there's an accident up ahead, he said. I'm going to have to turn and go back the long way, that okay with you, pal. I'll cut the meter here sure.

He'd become impatient like the rest of them.

I appreciate it, I said.

I took those kids on like my own, you know. I told everyone they were mine. Now they won't even see me. You got any, he asked.

Two, I said. Seven and five years old. My girlfriend was expecting the little one the last time I was in your cab.

I wouldn't remember that, he laughed. God knows how many fares I've had in here in the meantime.

I'm sure, I said.

No. Ruth hated London. I had a good job over there, making good money, a fleet of motors, holidays to Dubai. The money was unbelievable. It would shock you. I got a bit materialistic, I'm not afraid to say. We were taking out loans and living like king and queen, then it turned out she was being sly.

How so?

Writing fake invoices. Saying they were from court witnesses using my cabs. The cash was going into an account she'd set up. She was using fake names, the lot. She got time and wormed her way out of it. By that time we were back here, and me left with nothing. The shirt on my back and little else. Think how ashamed I was to go to my mother and tell her she was right all along.

Sure you can't help who you fall for, I said. You were decent, taking on her kids and giving them that lifestyle.

He frowned. Yes, he said. Then the bitch got out of it because the taxi firm was mine. She framed me.

God, what happened then, I asked Stephen.

I had to do time, didn't I! Stitched up like a kipper, you know. Million quid scam. They couldn't account for the whole of it.

That's awful!

He nodded, he pulled into my street.

How long did you get?

225

Six years, out in three. It's shocking what someone you once loved and trusted can do to you. I hope you have better joy with your missus.

Just over here, I said and he pulled up.

I recognise this house now, he said and he looked it over. Your fascia, he said, don't you find that a ball-ache?

What's that, I said getting my wallet out of my back pocket.

The wood. Wouldn't you be better getting the UPVC? You don't have to maintain it, it's just…you paint that, and then in between being arsed, it looks like shite, you know?

I bit my tongue. There you go, hold on to the change, I said.

No, no, he said and searched for a few coins, his hard thick neck tensing.

Trudy was ready to head out to the water, just for a walk. I told her about the accident and she said she'd leave the car at home. Do you remember I met this taxi driver years ago, I asked her. She didn't. Well he was giving me a lift there and he was saying he'd been framed for fraud.

They're all framed, she said.

He got six years and now he blames the wife.

Don't you all, Trudy said and she grabbed her coat and left without so much as a kiss on the cheek, shouting back that she'd be an hour or two.

The kids were outside on the trampoline. There was a net surround but the zip never worked from the get-go. I made myself a salad and ate it at the window, waving out to them.

The girl came in straight away. Did you write your book, Daddy, she asked.

I wrote a bit of it, I said kissing her on the top of the head. The boy soared out, hitting his head on the corner of the boiler house. It was only a nick but it was deep. Holding a cloth to his head I tried calling Trudy. Her phone laughed like church bells on the counter.

I got the kids in the car and we started heading to A&E. I forgot about the tailbacks in town. They were moving the bashed up car. There was an ambulance at the side of the road, a woman in her seventies sitting with a blanket and paramedics around her.

Trudy, where are you, I said, thinking we might pass her.

You should have left a note, Daddy, my daughter said.

We'll be home in no time, I said.

Once we got to the hospital I managed to get through to Trudy at home. I'm taking a taxi, she said.

I told her it was a waste of cash, that it was a small hole and we were getting seen next.

Okay, she said sounding emptied.

We were at the hospital for three hours. They put glue in his head and gave him stickers.

What happened here, the doctor asked my daughter.

I noticed the bruise under her eye. What did happen to you, I asked.

A boy in class hit me, she said.

I've been away, I explained. I was only in through the door and my partner had to go out. She never said. She left her phone behind. What did the teacher say, I asked my daughter. Did you tell your mother?

She looked at the floor.

Why did this boy hit you, I asked her.

I don't know, she said.

I bet he likes you, said the doctor giving her a sticker too.

I sent the kids ahead, told them to wait at the main door. I said to the doctor, I hope you aren't treating my daughter when she's older because some boyfriend is knocking her about.

He looked at me singularly. I wanted to say more but I let it drop.

At home Trudy came out to meet us in the driveway, she lifted our son into the house. Come here till I see my brave soldier, she said.

The boy sat with us past bedtime to make sure he wasn't concussed. Trudy put our girl to bed and met me in the kitchen. I think it was an accident, Trudy

The Lonely Crowd - Issue Six

whispered, but I'll go and talk to her teacher tomorrow. I'll find out more. I'm sorry I left my phone here.

It's almost like you didn't want to be found.

I didn't know that would happen.

They're still young, I said. They still need us a lot.

We all still need each other, Trudy said.

And that is what we proceeded to do for the next five years, pull apart and come together. The kids grew. They didn't need us much at all. It was a slap in the face how fast it happened.

I rarely used cabs any more. The last time I saw Stephen I was in the back of his. Trudy and I had separate cars by then. Mine was in getting a new clutch. In his photo he'd aged a lot but his eyes looked the same. I was mindful of the fascia we'd got reconditioned. He never looked at it. We dropped my son off. Stephen watched as he walked into school.

I've three myself, he told me. All getting big now.

Yes, I said, it isn't long in happening.

I hadn't the same time for him. Only as a story, you understand. He had something bitter in him that wasn't pleasant to be around. You married, I asked him.

I was, he said, three times believe it or not.

So you're on the market?

Nah, he said, I've given up on all that. Once I had the ring on my finger I would get claustrophobic, he said. You know how it is.

But sure if you love someone, isn't it worth it?

That's not my experience.

Sure it's hard no matter who you are and what you have, and who you're with.

I'll have to take your word for it, he said. My kids were all with the last wife, Ruth. None with the other ones. Ruth doesn't let them see me anymore. Haven't seen them in years.

That's tough, I said.

You're telling me.

What age are they? (I knew they'd be adults by now.)

Hmm… (He couldn't remember.) The grandparents won't allow them to see me.

Sure it isn't up to the kids.

But the grandparents have them and they're loaded. The kids know which side their bread is butter, don't they? Ruth's parents badmouth me in front of them.

Why's that? If you don't mind me asking.

No, I don't mind at all, said Stephen. They loaned me money to start up a taxi firm in Chelsea. They had the kids while we got sorted, then the business went belly up and they never let off me with it.

Shit!

They fucken accused me of stealing from them, then it was investigated and they found out it was an account in Ruth's name. Their own daughter was doing the stealing.

That's awful, I said.

It was awful. To be honest, it wasn't that bad for Ruth. She got out after a while. It was someone else, someone, a business partner of ours who was really framing her.

Who was this?

I'm not going to name names.

I respect that, I said.

I was very disappointed in him. He was a tool. They put that fella away. He made a lot of mistakes but he did his time.

(Of course I'd looked Stephen Kent up. I knew there was no taxi firm. That he and Ruth had both worked for CPS. That pride of his was so thick it was unswallowable.)

And so were you and Ruth not able to put it behind you, after?

She had someone else by then. She was always gorgeous. People would think I was her da. They'd all look at her when we were out anywhere. I'd be proud as punch.

Wouldn't you move heaven and earth to see your kids?

I have. I always had that fatherly thing about me. My parents had ten kids. I'm the oldest.

That's a lot.

I thought I'd be a dad, but just two kids, because our folks had no time for us you know. They just popped kids out. My father was a prick and my mother, she let him give her dog's abuse, you know.

You couldn't get away with that now.

No, you can't, said Stephen. My mother always hated Ruth. I found it wrong when I saw the two of them as being so alike. The shit they'd put up with from men. I wanted to give Ruth and the kids everything. They didn't have much to begin…well, the kids weren't mine biologically. They were, I don't want you to think badly of her, but they had different dads.

Ah, no, sure it's not like I know her. I'm not about to judge the girl.

Ruth's parents were very tight with her, said Stephen. She really deserved a lot more than she had. We all do, if I'm honest. We should have more than our lot and not feel bad about wanting that. We give up enough, don't you think? If we ever had it to begin with. I want for nothing these days. He pulled up outside my work, scratched the side of his hard thick neck. Anyway, Ruth has someone else now. I hope he knows what a lucky bastard he is.

The Package
Mark Blayney

There was a parcel on the step. Cathy tried to pick it up with her spare hand and was surprised at how heavy it was; leaving it, she pushed the door. Jim wielded a knife at a large fish, laid on a slab and staring gormlessly. Get on with it then, the creature's open mouth seemed to say.

'Sorry I'm late.'

Jim glanced up. 'Not sure how to tackle this, to be honest.' The fish's expression gave him no clues.

'Why not just use foil and bung it in the oven?'

Jim raised an agreeing finger as Cathy put her briefcase on the floor. She sat at the dining table and eased off her shoes. Jim struggled with a sheet of foil which unravelled faster than expected from its box and tore diagonally as he attempted to slice it with the lid open. 'That'll do,' he muttered, crumpling it around the fish, which looked rather crestfallen to be bundled so ignominiously into its final resting place.

'There's a parcel outside,' Cathy said, taking her unread newspaper from the case and flicking through rapidly.

'Already?' He rushed out; his socks were dark with wet when he returned clutching the package in both hands. The table rocked back and forth when he put it down. Cathy, feeling it was expected of her, asked what it was.

'Guess.'

'Too tired.' She hooked her skirt up and unrolled her tights while Jim studied the package. 'Where's the knife?' He turned and slipped on the kitchen tiles, his hand flailing towards the knife that was balanced on the edge of the worktop. It spun towards him and the handle neatly fitted into his hand. Cathy looked at the package suspiciously as Jim sliced the string tie and gingerly cut along the paper wrapping.

'Fragile, is it?'

'I don't want to damage it.' Two sturdy shells of polystyrene inside, which split like an egg. Jim shook the packaging free, polystyrene flaking off and squeaking before scattering around the box like snow. He reached in and carefully placed a slab of jagged grey concrete on the table.

For God's sake, Cathy thought.

'It's a piece of Berlin wall.'

'I guessed.'

'A genuine slab of history.'

'You'd hope so,' she said. 'I'd worry if you were buying just any old lump of defaced masonry.'

'Exactly.' Jim brushed the surface free of remaining polystyrene.

'Where did you get it?'

'eBay.'

'Ah.'

Flexing her toes on the kitchen floor, Cathy pulled a bag of peas from the freezer and switched the kettle on.

'I'm on the case with that.'

'It's okay, I'm just hungry.' She tipped too many peas into the saucepan and scooped some back, then put the bag away after tugging with the freezer door which didn't want to open. Jim tried to read a fragment of orange graffiti, his head turned sideways. The lettering had eroded and was difficult to make out; also his German was not as good as Cathy's. 'What does this say?'

Cathy shrugged. She tipped water into the pan and watched the peas hiss and spit, enjoying the brief feeling of steam on her face. Jim held the piece of wall and looked round for somewhere to put it.

Headless and filleted, the semi-detached fish lay hemmed in on the plate by its own tail and spine. Cathy toyed with her vegetables patiently while Jim chose a CD. He settled as the music emerged from unexpected corners of the kitchen and for a while there was silence as the fish was dispatched on its eternal voyage.

'Did you get the interview?'

Cathy paused, then nodded. 'Last week of January.'

'Fantastic.' He raised his glass. 'You must be thrilled.'

'And it could start in March.'

'Really?'

'So we'll have to get cracking with selling. If I get it,' she added.

'Yes.' He turned the fish head so its expression could not be seen; its milky eye now gazed at the ceiling instead.

'You'll like it there.' She leant across the table. 'I promise, you'll like it.'

'Mmm. If you get it.'

'Ah, well.' She enjoyed the taste of the fish, and pulled a slender, transparent bone from her teeth. 'If.'

Cathy poured wine into her favourite heavy glasses. Jim came down from the bathroom and rummaged in the hallway. 'Have you seen my coat?'

'In here.'

'Ah.' He took it from the back of the sofa. 'Not staying with me?' Cathy asked, sipping the wine.

Jim clapped his gloved hands together. 'Just an hour. Promise.' He put his boots on in the hallway, murmured a silent apology as he got mud on the carpet, and went out to the garden. There was ice on the path. We might get a white Christmas, he thought as he made his way to the ghostly image of the shed. Opening the door and pulling the cord, he smelt the new pine and saw the dust float across the bare space, lit by a naked bulb swinging gently. There was one roof panel left to fit, although, looking through at the stars, he felt a desire to leave it as it was.

Maybe I'll make it a window, he considered, before dismissing the thought as it would make the roof harder to insulate and felt. He took the panel from where it rested along the wall, went outside and climbed the stepladder.

He could see his breath in front of him. Daft time to build a shed, middle of winter. He lined it up, knocked the remaining nails in, climbed back down and picked up the nails he'd dropped on the hard ground. Back in the shed he looked round with pride, seeing where the workbenches and shelves were going to go.

Cathy watched a documentary on Roald Dahl then felt dozy on the wine. She glanced at her watch and went to the garden door. 'Jim?'

The shed was a faint cube, lit with a bright yellow square, its newness making it resemble an alien object that had landed overnight. Her shoes slipped on the path and she knocked on the door. He opened it in surprise. 'You don't have to knock, you know.'

'Very impressive.' She stepped in.

'Not bad for two weeks, eh?'

She walked round as if inspecting a flat to rent. 'What are you going to do in here?'

'Oh you know. This and that.'

'Well. Are you coming in tonight?'

*

He placed his hands round the offered glass of wine.

'You're cold.'

'I need a radiator in there. I've seen some portable ones in Ikea.' He rotated the glass, gaining warmth as much from the rich red colour as from the fire.

She hugged him. 'Bed?' He nodded.

Taking her pyjamas from the radiator Cathy noticed the piece of Berlin wall sitting squarely on the dressing table. 'Very funny.' She climbed into bed and shivered. Jim was downstairs: she heard the familiar sounds, the fridge door opening, the carving knife on the table. 'Just a quick nibble,' she could see him saying, getting the cheese and pickle. 'Up in a minute.'

The lump of wall seemed to look at her. 'I'm not having it there,' she resolved, jumping out of bed and looking round. She bent her knees as she lifted it with both hands. 'It can go here,' she decided, reaching up and placing it on one of the shelves, 'then I don't have to look at it.' Hearing Radio 4 come on softly downstairs and the dining chair scraping back, she got into bed and turned out the light.

As she dozed she sensed him in the room, flailing in the dark as he undressed; the blast of cold air as he got in; the relaxing feeling of him snuggling up to her. She moved to accommodate the shapes and lines of his body and half-slept as they cuddled, unsure whether they were making love or not, his hand caressing her hip.

There was a crash in the night. It felt like something caving in beside her, as if a meteorite had struck the house, or the ground had subsided. Is it one of those small earthquakes, she vaguely wondered, that you hear about? She slid towards Jim on a diagonal.

He scrabbled for the light and jumped from the bed. He saw the broken glass shelf, shards splintered across the bed and carpet, and in the centre of the bed the piece of Berlin wall, between the impression of his body and Cathy's frightened, foetal shape. She froze, then looked behind her to the remains of the shelf.

'Careful,' she said as Jim walked barefoot towards the broken glass.

'Why did you put it there?'

She moved round the wall and jumped off the bed. 'Why did I put it there? Why can't you build a shelf that actually stays up?'

He knelt and collected glass in his hand; as she spoke he did it carelessly so that jagged blades cut him. 'It wasn't designed to support something that heavy.'

'God's sake!' The realisation that she could have died mounted in her throat and made her shake. 'Shelves that don't stay up. Home-made sheds in the garden.'

'Cathy...'

'I just want us to get out of this claustrophobic little house that's—'

'It's not claustrophobic. It took us a long time to—'

'—full of junk.'

'And it's not little.'

Cathy lifted the rock from the centre of the bed. It left a deep, exact impression, like a crater. 'How did it miss me?' she wondered, glancing across her side of the bed to the damaged wall.

'It's the height of the shelf.' He straightened up and placed shards of glass on the dressing table. 'Any higher and it would have hit me on its way down. Any lower and it would have got you. Lucky, I suppose.'

What's it for, she wondered as he tried to translate another piece of indecipherable writing. It symbolises something for him, but what? What is it about men that they have to have things, they have to have objects, that they define themselves by?

'What does this mean?' he asked, pointing at the ink scrawl. She shook her head. Is it even real, she wondered as she poured two bowls of cornflakes and scattered raisins across them. Some raisins fell in the gap between the bowls. It wouldn't take much to find a bit of concrete and fake it, and say it's the Berlin wall. How much did he pay for it, she wondered.

It doesn't matter, she decided as they both crunched cornflakes and looked at each other. The important bit of it, the bit that means something, is the bit that's in his head.

Jim sat the piece of wall on the kitchen table. 'I'll take it out to the shed later,' he said, patting the concrete lovingly. He wrapped some of the glass in newspaper and broke up more so it would fit in the bin. 'What shall we do for lunch?'

'Not sure,' she said distractedly. 'Something quick?'

Later, in the shed, she found him drilling holes in the walls. 'I'm sorry about earlier. You're very good at DIY.'

'It's okay.'

'What are the holes for?'

'Ah!' Well—' he held her by the waist, and directed her out through the door. 'You see where the shed lines the fence. I'm going to run a wire across there, then I can send it up into the kitchen.'

'Why?'

'So I can get the shed powered up. Put a computer in here, and do some buying and selling.'

She smiled. 'You mean sit on eBay all night.'

'Well… not all night.'

'If I get that job…'

'I know. I know.' It hung between them, the 'you might not though'. He didn't want to say it, she could tell.

'I'll never see you.'

'What nonsense. And look—' he shepherded her
back into the shed, and she took small steps as he pushed
her a little too energetically— 'I thought we could put
some of your pictures up.'

'Oh… really?'

'It's silly keeping them in the loft. Isn't it?'

'They're not very good.'

'Cathy, they're fabulous, you know they are.' He
pressed her waist as he looked at the empty spaces on the
walls, seeing natural places for pictures between the
vertical struts. 'They'll be a couple of workbenches in
here so you could start painting again, if you wanted to.
No mess in the house.'

She wriggled away from him and held the door.
'Don't think so.'

'But you were really good.'

'Jim, I was a student then. I don't have time any
more for messing about painting pictures.'

'Not when you've got a proper job, eh.'

'Exactly.' She blew him a kiss; the cloud of breath
hovered in the air after she had gone.

He closed the door by pulling it towards him and
clipping the piece of wire around the hook. 'Have to put
a proper latch on here.'

Cathy had taken over lasagne duties from Jim but the
kitchen wasn't really big enough. Limp yellow squares
like impossible slices of cheese rested on pan edges. Jim

opened the post at the dining table. 'Look,' he said, but being at a critical stage in the operation she didn't turn round. 'A card from Val and Edwin. "Happy anniversary, hope to see you soon, how time flies!"'

'Bit early, aren't they?'

'They probably think it'll get slowed down in the Christmas rush.' He looked up. 'Do you think we should have a party? Invite everyone we haven't seen since the wedding.'

'If I get the job…'

'Yes. Well. I suppose. We could plan the party anyway, just in case—'

'There'll be so much to sort out. Visas…' she said vaguely. 'All kinds of stuff. We won't have time for parties.'

'Mmm. What about a theme? A Seventies theme.'

'Why Seventies?'

'Well, you know. It's what people do.'

'Sometimes I get the impression you don't want me to get this job.'

'It's not that.'

They looked at each other. What is a legal commissioner anyway, Jim wondered. Too late to ask now. If she thinks it's been five years and I still don't know what she does all day, she'll think I'm an idiot. 'I'll be honest with you,' he said, opening his palms towards her. 'I like it here.'

'I know.'

'I really don't want to move. Not to Luxembourg, anyway.'

'You won't be.'

'Eh?' A light came into his eyes. He looked hopeful. He looked happy.

'It's Brussels.'

'I thought Brussels was in Luxembourg?'

'Brussels is in Belgium.'

'Where's Luxembourg then?'

'Luxembourg.' She tried to say it without sounding sarcastic, but it was difficult.

'Yes, but where's it in?'

'In? It's in Luxembourg.'

He absorbed this. 'Luxembourg is in Luxembourg?'

'Yes.'

'Well I never.'

He opened another letter. A silence, which he tried to defuse. 'You definitely want to go, then?'

Her mouth was a horizontal line, long and thin; a symbol in a mathematical equation, Jim uncertain what it might mean. Like in books at school: symbols, mysterious and magical and beyond his understanding, frightening even; yet why was this, they were just marks on a page. He picked the card up again and tapped it on the table. 'I like being here. I like the town, and the river. I like being able to drive up to the—'

'Yes.'

'I want us to be here. Have kids. Like we—'

The water boiled over and Cathy jumped up. 'We will. Just there, rather than here.' She took the pan off the boil. 'Lots more room. And I'll be doing something I love.'

'You'll be so busy.'

'I promise,' she said. 'We'll think about a family when I'm settled.'

'What about me?' he said plaintively.

'It'll be better for both of us. And,' she added persuasively, 'you can do your job anywhere, can't you?'

'Yes, you're right.'

She laid the pasta slabs on the lasagne dish, opened the oven and through a cloud of steam put the pan on the centre tray. The door closed with a snap. Remind me what I am again, Jim thought. Sometimes I forget myself.

'The thing is... look,' she said, the piece of wall still on the table, 'do you think you could get rid of that?'

'Yes.' Jim took the bin out as the fish remains had begun to smell, then went to the shed. When he had gone she cleared some boxes from the hallway. More stuff he had been buying at car boot sales. 'People don't understand how much this stuff is worth!' he said, his face glowing. In the shed, she told him, in the shed. He looked hurt; perhaps she had spoken too sharply.

She called but he didn't answer. He had no lights on even though it was getting dark. Is this lunch or dinner, she wondered. She used oven gloves to take the lasagne to the table; then had to take it back because the wall was still there. When she was sure he wasn't going to come in unexpectedly, she took the letter from its hiding place behind the washing machine.

'It is with great pleasure,' the letter began. She liked reading it, over and over, seeing the shape of the words. 'It is with great pleasure.'

She poured wine. 'I'll bring him round,' she told herself, feeling a surge of optimism at a brilliant orange sunset. 'When we're in the new place, he can keep it in the living room.' Her voice echoed on the garden walls when she called. It got dark, and she called again. She went down the path to find out what was up.

Two Poems
Jackie Gorman

The Moorhen

A twitching bird with a pointed beak,
the moorhen nested near our house,
at the water's sunlit edge.
In her nest, I saw my father's death.
There was grey hair, a red cardigan button,
a black pen and a brain haemorrhage.
Cow parsley drowned in the clogged capillaries.
Shock, the colour of ox blood, bound to the heart.
The perfumed stench of impermanence lingered.

Badlands

The badlands of the painted desert
with black velvet skies and
floating liquid birdsong.
There's the distant sound of dancing
being swallowed into the desert floor.
Muffled rhythms switch off
the beehive in my brain.
The hot silence says hold on,
like a dried up creek waiting for rain.
That is to say, let go of wanting,
endure but hold on, let go.
Rain is coming soon.

Flood
Paul Davenport-Randell

More talisman than investment – with Cassie's approval
Ted leaped in and bought the small holding. It was found
at the end of a dirt track, flanked on both sides by black-
water ditches. They were more than a mile from their
closest neighbours across the low-lying fen one way, two
and a half miles from the village the other.

The plot consisted of a ramshackle house, a garage
and twenty acres of land, two-thirds of which they
dedicated to the keeping of a hundred or so chickens and
three nanny goats. Another acre they gave over to
growing daffodils. They sold the eggs the hens laid to
local farm shops and convenience stores, the milk from
the goats, too. Cassie bunched the flowers with elastic
bands and together with an honesty box displayed them
on a fold-down table at the entrance to the dirt track.

The first months were the hardest. Glad of the
distraction, Ted committed himself more enthusiastically
than Cassie – who mostly tended to the needs of their
son.

Foxes, Ted found, were the major problem. One
night alone he lost five birds to these predators. The half-
devoured carcases that he found up by the hedgerow he
bagged and incinerated in a blazing oil drum, as an

instruction manual he had picked up recommended. To prevent them digging under the fence again, he lowered the chicken-wire and buried its hem a whole foot deeper under the ground.

This appeared to do the trick. Every morning for two weeks, Ted walked the fence, and although he saw signs of digging, it was not breached.

He felt good again. His raised spirits permeated through to Cassie. That night she agreed to share a bottle of wine. They got a little drunk, and for the first time in a long while their talk was amicable, and Cassie did not allude to his affair. Once, she even laughed at something he said, and Ted dared to feel a little hopeful. But all too suddenly she became serious again, and went up to check on Lucas, and did not come down.

Before long Ted discovered two more hens with their hearts torn out. He pounded furiously around the perimeter fence, cursing the blasted animals who had done this. He found no holes dug anywhere. This baffled him.

He stayed up all night. He watched from the window. In the early hours they came, a vixen and her litter. She sniffed around the fence, while her pups rolled around playfully under the gaze of the nanny goats. Most of the birds were inside the shed and gave no cries of alarm. He watched the fox make several attempts at clawing at the dirt, but without success. Eventually she gave up, gathered her litter, and the three of them disappeared through the hedgerow.

But the following morning he found another bird savaged, this time inside the fence. He scratched his head, he clenched his jaw. If not the foxes, then what?

Again he dropped the hen's limp body into a plastic bag, ready for cremation. He fetched an armful of logs, a fistful of kindling. A can of lighter fuel. He approached the oil drum, stood behind the shed, and was within a few feet when he saw scurrying up the length of wood sticking out the rim of the drum, a rat. It was a big, plump thing and it moved quickly, leaping to the ground and squeezing through a hole in the back of the shed, around which Ted noticed a tuft of feathers.

Ted blocked the hole with cement.

Both the fence and the shed held firm after that. For several months the only casualties were those ones who died of natural causes. Or weaker birds. Those the others bullied and pecked at and prevented from fattening. This, said the instruction manual, was quite normal behaviour. Survival of the fittest.

At long last Ted felt confident he was doing things right, that he was making a success of the smallholding. Their income was small, but adequate. They did not go hungry. Cassie began to look happy again. She smiled more, had more energy, in the way she had before they had Lucas. She let him, Ted, eat at the table with them again. Instead of taking turns to entertain their son, they played with him together. And if Ted dared to appear happy, pleased with himself, she no longer made spiteful comments to remind him of his place, their arrangement, their reason for moving out here, away from the city, away from *her*.

Winter came, snowfall. This provided Ted a new job. Each morning he shovelled snow from the track into the ditches. It was vital he kept it clear: if the track was impassable, Cassie could not deliver the eggs and milk, nor drop Lucas off at pre-school in the village, where he now went three mornings a week. This Ted had learned the hard way, and had to call on Joe and his tractor from Thornwood Farm to pull their Audi out of the mud on two occasions.

'A flash car's no good to you in this business,' Joe told Ted. 'You need to get yourself a Jeep. Save yourself from breaking your back and filling them ditches to busting. In these parts, if your ditches go, you're in trouble.'

Though Cassie prohibited him driving from the Audi, it was the one thing that still connected him to his old life. The one thing that reminded him of the successful man he had been, who he was, and what he was about. Some days he would sneak into the garage just to look at it, to lay a hand upon it. Some things he found harder to let go than others, but in the end, he understood it was one more sacrifice he must make for the greater good.

When the daffodils unfurled and along the tops of the banks of the ditches – in which the black-water was higher than ever – the first wild flowers of spring burst open, Ted found all his newly hatched chicks gone. He had brought in a cockerel to help in the matter of replenishing the lost stock. He looked, but found no sign of the chicks anywhere. He was completely stumped.

'I need to ask Joe's advice,' he told Cassie, and after long consideration, she agreed to let him go, and Ted left the perimeters of the smallholding, alone, for the first time since their arrival.

Joe was working the fields. It was a busy time of year. He would not be back before sunset.

'If it's about your birds, I might be able to help,' offered Joe's daughter. She let him into the kitchen. She made them tea. They sat across the table from one another. She had attended agricultural college. Now she helped her father. One component of the course consisted of poultry and battery farming.

Ted explained everything. His inexperience. The setbacks. The disappearances. He barely stopped to take breath. With the brief exception of her father, he had not spoken to anyone other than his wife and son in two years. He stayed longer than he intended.

It was getting dark when he returned. He carried in from the car under his arm one of the rolls of nylon netting he had purchased. He told Cassie he had had to go to the hardware merchants on the outskirts of the city, twenty miles away. None of the local stores supplied what he needed. He did not know why the books had not mentioned it, why he had not thought of it himself. Their problem was most likely predators of the winged kind: owls, sparrowhawks, marsh harriers. In his free hand, he held a bunch of flowers. Cassie's icy stare thawed. Ted exhaled.

The summer was a relatively dry one. The depth of the water in the ditches receded. They lost no more birds to raiders of any nature. Ted allowed their numbers to increase and they began producing more eggs. On Saturdays, Ted now made the deliveries, while Cassie took Lucas on the bus to the swimming pool, to the city. It was important he learned to swim, as Ted never had. A skill for life, they agreed.

With extra money coming in, Cassie returned from the city with treats. She might cook them steak, or a venison stew. Roast a shoulder of lamb on a Sunday. Never chicken: they laughed and agreed it felt, for them, akin to cannibalism. Twice a week they drank a bottle of wine with dinner. Lucas got new toys, new books. She bought Ted thermal socks, a new sweater, for added warmth when the weather turned cold again. On the night of his birthday, as the first flurry of snow fell, she invited him to her bed.

Next day Ted found one of the nanny goats lain in the snow, mauled, bloody, barely recognisable. The ecstasy he had woken with was snuffed out in a moment. He fell to his knees and cursed the heavens. What beast could have left such a mess? He could not begin to imagine. This was the English countryside, not the Serengeti. At the end of his tether, Ted drove the new Jeep to Thornwood Farm, to once more seek advice.

He told Cassie the only explanation Joe had to offer. It was rumoured a big cat prowled these parts. Perhaps it had escaped from the zoo, and embarrassed the zoo had kept it a secret. Or it had been an illegal, exotic pet, gifted as a kitten, then let loose when it became too big and too expensive to feed. There had been sightings. A blurred photograph had appeared in the local press. Nothing conclusive. Joe loaned him a shotgun. A box of cartridges.

For five successive nights Ted again sat at the kitchen window. The shotgun rested, its muzzle broken, both barrels charged, ready, on the butcher's block by the door. He remained vigilant. He saw no movement. Nothing to alert him. Nothing to suddenly widen his increasingly sleep-heavy eyelids. Over the course of days, his temperament became evermore fractious. Cassie warned him he was becoming obsessed. She tried to reassure him. She tried telling him to relax, before he made himself ill. What good would he be to her and Lucas then?

But he would not be told.

'I'm the provider!' he bit back at her. 'Me! That's my role – remember?'

There, at the window, he drifted off.

He gave a start when Cassie shook him awake.

'There's someone here to see you,' she told him. He was too exhausted to recognise the coldness in her tone. 'She says she has something you might want to see.'

Through the window he saw a muddied Range Rover. Beside it stood a young woman. He could see her hot breath clouding before her. She rubbed her hands against the chill. Above her, the sky was darkening.

Ted leapt up off his chair and hurried outside. The young woman smiled and swung open the back door on the trunk of her vehicle.

'I think that's your problem solved,' she said.

Ted peered inside. At once he felt a sensation of relief and elation surge through him. He grabbed the young woman in his arms and embraced her close to him.

Smiling, he watched her drive away. He felt the first drops of rain on his forehead. He turned, and saw Cassie standing at the window, Lucas clutched to her.

She questioned him soon as he walked through the door. 'Who was she?'

'Joe's daughter,' he said.

'Why have you never mentioned her?'

He thought he knew the answer but he could not say it. He knew how it looked. He felt his face flush. He could do nothing to stop it. He wished he had not hesitated.

'I'm sure I have mentioned her.'

She continued to stare at him. Her face said everything, and nothing at all. Rain lashed the window. He could hear it on the roof. Heavy. Relentless. Unforgiving.

'I'm going upstairs,' she said.

'Night-night, daddy,' said Lucas, and he clenched and unclenched his fist as his mother carried him from the room.

It was not a noise that woke him. It was a deep, penetrating silence.

Usually there was something: Lucas mumbling in his sleep in the room one side; from the other, the creak of the bed or the shuffle of crisp sheets as Cassie turned over, or occasionally talking as she dreamt; the cluck of a nocturnal feeder coming from the coop; the baying of the goats; the odd lone late traveller on the road at the end of the track; the wind howling under the eaves; rainwater running in the guttering – but there was not one solitary note of sound.

He went to the window. Outside he could not see a thing. There were no shapes he could make out. Not the silhouette of the hedgerow against the night sky. Nor the low roof of the garage or the taller chicken shed. There was no dome of dark nebulous orange over the village that could usually be seen in the distance. All there was was a black, flat, still emptiness. It was as though someone had upturned the house, and looking down was like staring up into a void of starless space.

He pulled on his bathrobe. He went into Lucas's room. He tried the light switch. Nothing. He fetched the torch he had taken to keeping on the cabinet beside his bed. He shone it onto his boy's bed. It was empty, the pillow askew, bedcovers drawn untidily back. In Cassie's room, the same. No slumbering, softly breathing body under the sheets. He pointed the beam at the closet. The door was wide. Inside was a rail of coat hangers. That was all.

'Cassie?' he called out. His voice did not seem to carry far. 'Cassie? Lucas?'

He was five steps down the staircase when his bare foot dipped into a wet, icy coldness. Shining the torch, its white light reflected back at him on a surface of water, deeper than the ground floor ceiling. Deeper than his own height. Floating on the top were a dozen or so wilted daffodils.

In his bedroom, he raised the sash. Below him, there was still that nothingness. It crossed his mind to leap, but he could not tell what he might be leaping down upon. Certainly the flood was all about him. How far it stretched beyond the fen, beyond the river and the marshland, how many miles, and what sharp objects had been dragged along on its surging tide when the river broke its banks – were unknowns. Even if he could swim, he could not predict how far he would have to go to reach dry land. Or if he would make it at all. He had no life raft.

Torch in pocket, feet balanced on the sill, he reached up, feeling for the guttering. His fingers found its concave edge. He gripped, tugged. He had one foot off the sill when he felt the guttering give.

He thought he would fall. He cried out, and lunged at the window frame, caught its edge, and holding on for dear life, swung out over the abyss. Below him, the guttering made a splash. He swung towards the window again, and, shaken, clambered back inside.

For a moment, he stood out on the landing. He thought he heard the sound of a helicopter. It was far off, but he was certain it was there: rising and then quickly receding again, to be replaced once more by silence.

But the sound had driven his gaze upwards. And he remembered – rather than saw – the hatch into the attic. He brought his bedside cabinet out and placed it under the hatch. He stood upright on top of it. He stretched himself as tall as he was able on the tips of his toes. He pushed the door aside. In one small leap, he caught hold of the sides of the hatch, and pulled himself upwards and through.

Stepping carefully across the beams, torch lighted, he moved along until he found a place where the felt underlay overlapped. With effort, he tore at the felt, stripped away enough so that now he could see the undersides of the roof tiles. He removed one, and a puddle of darkness as deep as the one he was submerged in poured through.

He removed two more tiles. The darkness spread. A coldness enveloped him. Soon he made a hole large enough to climb out through.

Ted sat on the red-tiled roof in his bathrobe. He surveyed everything around him, searching for something recognisable, a landmark: the roof of the out-buildings or the conical peaks of the silos on Thornwood

Farm, the thinnest cut of the moon. But there was nothing.

The light from his torch flickered, then went out. He drew his knees up to his chest. He waited.

He waited.

Lucca: Last Days of a Marriage
Tom Vowler

Even mid-morning the heat is the wrong side of tolerable. An ambient ferocity that consigns him to torpor between short bursts of activity, the discrete parts of the day bound by the searing onslaught. He'd left the hotel an hour ago, the *wap wap* of the room's fan still occupying like rotor blades some frontier of his mind. He starts, as Pollex's characters had, encircling the town along its walled walkway, stopping at each bastion, grateful for the leafy shade on offer. He felt the narrative ambled at this point, became part-travel guide as it documented how the wall was designed by Leonardo, how each of its four sides was given over to a different species of tree. The stonework, an actual guidebook informs him, acts today as a liminal boundary, dividing ancient from modern, contemporary life held at bay where possible. Pollex reminds readers the town had once rivalled Florence for prominence, that Caesar himself visited, Dante too while in exile. He could, of course, now edit such detail, mute the verbiage to his own satisfaction, the only reins a ghostly voice he is obliged to hear.

A young couple kiss against a centuries-old trunk, incautious, solipsistic. From their lack of wilting he

figures them locals, Tuscans for whom the heat is a
frivolous matter, who know nothing of wet Tuesday
mornings on the M25. He imagines what it would take to
interrupt them, what measure of sound or force would
untwine the pair, remembers on some level the
exhilaration they are feeling. It's not that he begrudges
them exactly; more that he wishes to point out love's
inexorable arc.

He removes his hat, fans himself before walking
on. On waking he had been surprised at the absence of a
hangover, and the assessment had indeed been
premature, the sun now drawing it from deep in him and
for a moment he thinks he might be sick. *Cretino!*

A waft of sweet *buccellato* arrives from below, and
after pretending to himself that he is hungry, he takes the
next set of steps down into the old town.

His task, he supposes, is an unusual one, though
literature boasts its share of posthumous publications,
books part-finished, part-edited upon the author's
demise. That Pollex set much of the novel in Tuscany
was, initially, a source of delight on learning he would be
required to visit, to immerse himself in the region's
underbelly, let *la terra* permeate him. Much of the book's
closing chapters take the form of notes, and so it was
deemed necessary to work on it *in situ*, to strive for a
resonant denouement. But the undertaking has now
become burdensome, not least because Pollex's

characters were witnessing a marital collapse to mirror his own.

He'd worked with Pollex for the first couple of novels, books that sold in moderate number, establishing the man as a seasoned mid-lister, unremarkable yet in possession of a steady and loyal readership. His own poor health had seen a parting of ways for the next work, a colleague stepping in, presiding over what turned out to be Pollex's 'breakthrough' book, a genre-bending tale set in post-apocalyptic Glasgow that bore no resemblance to the lyrical realism preceding it. Had it been a debut, nobody would have touched it, least of all his own publishing house; they were simply honouring a contract, assembling a novel they suspected wouldn't sell.

But sell it did. Despite an age of endless, readily available analysis, there exists little agreement as to why a book does well: a series of favourable reviews, celebrity book clubs, influential bloggers – all play their part, but guarantee nothing. Word-of-mouth is still the overarching factor, and how do you measure that? Within two months of publication, Pollex was the author everyone wanted to interview, to pastiche. The rights sold in thirteen countries, film options arrived soon after. Some of the parties are, he suspects, still going on now.

So it was a surprise when they asked him to return to edit *Lucca*, the locum colleague jettisoned at the author's request. From the early drafts, however, it was clearly going to be a difficult book: not at all the

anticipated sequel in terms of style or content; more a
return to his earlier *oeuvre* but with even less commercial
appeal. As the book's editor he was frequently drawn in
meetings to comment on its plot, its formula – its
comparisons to The Previous One – and he'd searched
hard for a balance between cryptic and tantalising. In
truth it was obvious Pollex regarded his departure an
artistic compromise too far, despite the economic
freedom it bestowed him with. It was as if he was saying,
Look I can write a bestseller if I want to. Now let me
return to the real stuff.

The sun is directly overhead now, chromic and
irrefutable. He needs to find a cafe, sit in shade and
rehydrate. Later, when it is cooler, he will drive up into
the hills to the north, navigate the serpentine road into
the Apuan Alps, where the marble Michelangelo himself
once quarried renders the great slopes as if snow-clad.
Then, if he's not too tired, onto the verdant valleys of
Garfagnana. Pollex mentions the region several times,
though his characters are too preoccupied by hostilities to
visit, its treatment in the book providing, he senses,
excessive adornment, self-congratulatory prose. And yet
he is drawn to the place simply from Pollex's vicarious
descriptions, a Shangri-La where, apparently, the silence
is absolute, the terrain timeless. He told Pollex on more
than one occasion that the allegory of the couple not
making it to the hills was strained, that why describe it

all if no action takes place there. But as with other
counsel he offered during their early editorial exchanges,
the sales of *Lucca*'s predecessor allowed Pollex to resist.

He takes a long drink from a fountain in the piazza, the
water rarefied, seemingly ancient, and he imagines it
cleansing him of toxins and memories, imagines
remaining under its flow for the rest of the day. It is only
when his stomach swells in discomfort and he senses an
audience that he withdraws his head and converges on a
nearby cafe.

He orders a coffee in Italian, the waiter responding
in English. What is it they pick up on? The attire, the
accent, the general unease in posture? And why English?
Couldn't he be Dutch or Finnish or Israeli? He once
quizzed a taxi driver on the matter the only other time
he'd visited the country.

You English are so polite, the man had said. An
Italian would be on his phone, telling someone where
and what he ate last night, which restaurant he was going
to this evening. But mostly it's the shoes. You wear such
bad shoes.

Vero.

When she left last year – a sudden though not
unexpected departure – his physical appearance became
a source of concern for the first time in a decade, the
separation ushering in a midlife crisis of sorts. Scrutiny
revealed tufts of errant hair accumulating from his

nostrils and ears, a stomach that bore testimony to endless lunches with authors – a culture of indulgence despite the suspicion people were about to stop buying books. His wardrobe, he realised, boasted a spectrum of beiges and browns, most of it bought more than five years ago. His hair, once profuse and lustrous, had long ago begun the retreat crown-ward.

He joined the gym, vowed to cycle to work. Researched what was fashionable, purchased some clothes he knew would remain unworn. In the end he settled for having his teeth whitened, a procedure that served only to draw attention to the weathering of his other features. *Grande cretino!*

Is there someone else, he had asked her as she packed that day, and he could see that there was.

He considers buying a paper, if only to parade it to the waiter when he returns, but such haughtiness is beyond him today. Instead he sits back, adjusts the chair to be in consistent shade. Above him, perhaps two floors up, there is some kind of commotion, an instant in which the natural order of things is displaced, and he looks up at the blaze of colour alighting from the wall. The departing jay, he realises, has a gecko writhing between its talons, the bird rising in near silence into the thermals. He looks around but is the only witness to this remarkable yet trivial spectacle. A few moments later the jay is little more than a speck over one of the town's churches, and then, despite the unbroken blue canopy, there is nothing.

Such a demise has its appeal, he thinks, swift and efficient, a final journey above all you have inhabited, the lizard oblivious on all but the most primal level to what was playing out, its brain eliciting a flush of chemicals to evoke fear, before… what? Resignation? Nothing? For his own amusement he bestows the gecko with superior cognisance, imagines it thinking: this is something that hasn't happened before. Of it being thrilled by this novel vantage point.

The waiter places his coffee down wordlessly, attends to another table. The absence of insincere small talk found in other countries is, he has discovered, refreshing, allowing him to fully attend to the melancholy. Pollex's couple had been here a little later in the year, when the town was immersed in its month of celebrations, the climax of which is the procession of the Holy Cross, a pageant that departs from San Frediano Basilica, a trail of *lumini*, a thousand candles and lamps snaking through the town to the cathedral. Again the symbolism is clumsy, Pollex using the parade to signify the journey his characters are on, the lights, on reaching the *Duomo*, finally extinguished.

The coffee, as ever, is good and he senses his hangover receding a little, vows to take up smoking again. He watches a middle-aged couple loiter in front of the Basilica, perhaps on the cusp of an argument. The standoff is broken, their ensuing embrace an extended

one. Above them is a golden mosaic, an enthroned Christ
and, after counting them, he supposes the Apostles. He
wonders if Pollex's frequent references to religion
represented something beyond character introspection,
that somewhere beneath the surface prose lay clues to the
author's fracturing mind.

He leaves some coins on the saucer. As young
lovers in Paris, they had once fled from a bistro without
paying. It wasn't planned, but they had little money and
the food had been ordinary, the service lacklustre. He'd
assumed she was joking, but the moment, fuelled by the
bottle of Chianti they'd shared, gained a silent traction,
and before he knew it they were shuffling towards the
door, giddy with the thrill of the thing, feeding off each
other's daring. They assumed nobody would notice,
imagined a gradual realisation at the end of the evening,
the English couple who'd had cassoulet and shared
dessert. An acceptable loss. But they were barely a
hundred yards away when one of the larger waiters burst
from the door behind them, shouting, running,
brandishing something. He'd wanted to turn back,
announce it was all a prank, but instead they ran and ran,
finally finding succour in a crowded bar where they
removed their jackets, melted in to the gloaming with a
large group of musicians. They'd sensed the man
occupying for a while the fringes of the room, but their
cover proved adequate. He never told her how afraid
he'd been.

He crosses the square, stops to watch a puppet show with a dozen others. He is in no hurry, Lucca – the ancient Lucca – one of the few cities to permit this. He cuts through the lattice of medieval streets, imagines Pollex imagining his characters, manipulating them to his aesthetic end. Occasional fissures between buildings afford a glimpse of the tree-topped Guinigi Tower, the town's totemic landmark, its lofty garden of oaks incongruous amid the firmament. He should climb the steps, count them as she tended to all considerable staircases, childlike in her tallying. Often, if descent failed to match in total accent, she would negotiate them again.

Did he know even then that he was only borrowing her? If he had, he chose to ignore it, ignore the sand as it fell through their hourglass. The someone else turned out to be a colleague, encountered on a research trip to Mexico; he hadn't wanted the details but she'd told him anyway. Old love rendered ordinary by new.

He emerges into a smaller square, a large poster boasting a Bob Dylan concert (though closer inspection reveals the date has passed), another reminding visitors that Puccini was born here. Below them a father and daughter set up a keyboard and amplifier, test the volume, the girl placing a soft hat on the ground. He thinks to listen for a while, sit somewhere, order a *bicchierino* of grappa. Instead he follows the signs to the botanical garden, judges it to be somewhere he can make notes on the manuscript.

The garden, a triangular plot in the south-west corner of the town, turns out to be small, the woman taking his money keen to point out that they still have more than two hundred species of plant. A pair of sculptured lions guard the gate above her. Inside there is a series of large ceramic medallions illustrating milestones in the garden's history, such as the planting of its prized Lebanon cedar in 1822. He locates the giant tree, stands beneath it, tries but fails to contemplate such longevity, its silent majesty commanding reverence. It is older than *War and Peace*, than *Moby-Dick*. On the grass beyond the tree, a small boy is trying to assemble some sort of glider, the child's face scrutinising the parts, as if not knowing where to start. He thinks to walk over, squat down and help, but deems this a source of potential disquiet in today's climate, the gesture doubted. Instead he finds a bench in some shade, takes out the parts of the book he has brought.

It was three days before anyone found Pollex, the garage not thought to be in use. The absence of a note seemed odd at first, a man who'd spent his life curating words, strangely silent. There had been a will, instruction left for the work-in-progress to be edited before publication, suggesting he'd intended to complete it first. To those on the outside there had been few if any signs. Rumours circulated, of a writer who sensed his creative well had run dry, who realised *Lucca* would be mauled by critics.

He wrote to Pollex's widow, offered commiserations to her and their children. She replied, declining the offer to have any input into the novel, remarking that she was sure he'd do a fine job.

He thinks of how he will tie up the loose ends, wonders what Pollex had in store for his couple; there seemed little prospect of reconciliation, and yet he is tempted to leave open the possibility. Pollex's agent was equally unaware of the man's state of mind, could shed no light on what path the final few chapters should take. As for the earlier sections, he'd apply the same process he would to a finished work, asking only, Can the book live without this? Regardless of how strong the writing was, how beautiful or poignant or insightful, if the answer was in the affirmative, it was culled.

Despite their working relationship – almost a decade if you discounted the two-year forced sabbatical – he had only actually met Pollex a handful of times. As writers went he was the usual mix of awkward outsider and engaging conversationalist, part romantic, part pragmatist. He came late to words, at least in terms of fiction, had lived several lives before early redundancy from a teaching post forced a replotting of the vocational odyssey. What struck him most when he first read Pollex was that he could write, really write; so many books he edited were conceptually and structurally and tonally strong, would sell in significant number, but which neglected the music of a sentence, its ability to be affective rather than merely expository. Abstract instead of just literal. Pollex, he felt, *troubled* his sentences into existence, cared for them as one might a prized possession, or one's child. He was a stylist who, until *Lucca* at any rate, knew when to get out of a sentence, knew when lyricism became onanism. The editor's role, of course, was to collaborate in this alchemy, a dance partner who neither led nor followed. An objective (though it rarely is) vision for the work, uncluttered by ego.

The boy has had some success and, after several abortive attempts to launch the glider, looks around for a parent to assist. Watching the scene play out, he feels only moderately saddened by the absence of his own children, is perhaps curious at the omission.

He wonders why Lucca. Why Pollex chose here to unravel a marriage. This Renaissance town of a hundred churches, so often besieged and occupied and sold. He wonders what fraught and terrible thoughts played out in the man's mind during those final hours.

The softest of breezes brushes across his forearm, gustless, barely anything. He pictures the jay in its nest opening up the gecko, the skin easily penetrated, its warm, sinewy interior shared among the bird's young. He thinks of the lovers he is yet to have, whether such presumption is arrogant at this stage of life. Wonders if the protective layer around his heart is any more substantial. He would like to have come here with her, perhaps in a cooler season, climb the tower, hire a tandem and slalom slowly along the fortress wall until the cicadas quietened and gave way to a distant aria.

Three Poems
Sue Moules

A Green Man Running

Always know a way out – the green man above the door
by the red fire hydrant knows the way.
In the ballroom there's a ticking noise that isn't a clock.

The professor of criminology knows the lawless mind
he's studied the psychology of arsonists.
In the ballroom there's a ticking noise that isn't a clock.

But no one says anything. When the alarm sounds
no one moves. The complacency of over practice.
In the ballroom there's a ticking noise that isn't a clock.

No one seems bothered. The green men are illuminated,
the piano plays sea shanties, boat rigging in the harbour
chimes
like the ticking noise that isn't a clock in the ballroom.

T. Rex

Marc Bolan with his made up eyes, dark ringlet hair
singing *Ride a White Swan,*
lead singer in a group named after a dinosaur.
Then he was killed in a car crash,
extinct, gone at the height of his fame.

Her grandson bought a bag of coloured dinosaurs.
Name them he said. She couldn't;
Ride a White Swan like the people of the Beltane,
but Audrey, Sharon, Stephanie, Alison, Jane
the girls in her class dancing in the long ago disco.

The Grey Road Passes Through the Hills

Take the second left,
turn right at the bridge
go up the hill until the road becomes a track,
turn through the forestry gate.

The cottage is ochre yellow with gothic windows
and the scent of baking bread.
Outside pine cones cluster,
wind wobbles through branches,
time stands still.

Magnolias
Bethany W. Pope

A pool of buttery light spills out from the wide window above the sink and Millie likes to curl her toes in it as she scrubs the supper dishes. She has gotten very careful with the knives, both because her youngest granddaughter pointed out (the last time she visited) that there were yellow globs of egg (dried hard as amber) in between the serrated teeth and because the skin of her hands has grown thin and tender as wet paper. Millie trusts doctors (after all, her father was one) but she despises paying for their services. The cost of everything has grown unaccountably high. She doesn't think of herself as cheap, just careful.

Looking out, Millie can see the wide flat leaves of the magnolia, their waxy green interspersed with brown, hairy buds the size of a cigar. Soon, if the branches are allowed to follow their nature, the yard will fill with the sharp scent of lemons and for a month her view will be filled with a thousand hanging moons the size of dinner plates. She will go out, in the evening when her husband is asleep, and sit on the porch. The padded bench will settle lovingly around her wide buttocks and the thick, paint-stripping coffee she brews will warm her guts even as it continues the slow work of dissolving the inner wall of her stomach. She never had the chance to learn to brew coffee when she was a girl (they had servants for that) and she hasn't learned since. She doesn't care. She's learned to like the taste of her work. When the flowers come, Millie will sit and breathe in the darkness, her mind murmuring music that she has always chosen not to understand.

They've lived in this house for thirty years. Before that, they had a much smaller place on the other side of town where their neighbours were, sometimes, middle-class blacks and Millie was uncomfortable inviting her better-off church friends home for a glass of sugary tea.

Bill would never have been able to afford a place like this on his own, no matter how hard or long he worked. Nowadays, it seems, mechanics climb the green rungs of the social ladder much more easily. Some of their neighbours began with grease under their nails (though most of them were lawyers and surgeons) but when they married, when Millie and Bill were flushed with the liquor of consummated love, it was a very different story. Millie's father cut them off as soon as the ink was dry on their marriage licence (she was hardly even showing) and the next thing that nineteen-year-old knew she was sitting barefoot, pregnant, and blushingly pretty on the inside of a chrome coloured trailer house perched on a parched-bare red plate of dry Georgia soil.

Bill was good at his job. Millie knew that he would be. Her thin, beak-nosed boy could sing with his hands.

He earned money, and fast. They moved out of the trailer and into a one-storey house with a cracked-concrete foundation. Millie never complained. She was happy enough with him. But maybe Bill had expected a little more out of life when he married her. His dark eyes quickly grew a raptor's hood, his mouth turned mean about the edges, and although he kissed her, sometimes, even after the babies came, she seldom felt the love-flutter of his thrumming heart when he did it, and his fingers only seemed to flex at work.

Things improved, a little, when the children were grown. Soon after the first one was out of the house (his law-school bills caused Bill to pace a thin grey strip in the rug) Millie got a telegram from the mother whose voice she hadn't heard in twenty years. Her father was dead. Millie was invited to the reading of the will.

She dressed in her best, unaware that she looked like her oldest sister's maid in her day-off clothes, and laughed away her knowledge that her aging siblings were going out of their way not to look at her, focusing their eyes on the flower in her decades-out-of-date pillbox hat. One of the hangovers from the early years of her marriage was that she only bought clothes when she absolutely had to.

The lawyer was broad and fat in every feature, but he had a bit of Bill in the sour corners of his mouth. He read out the terms like someone was pulling out his intestines. Her siblings smiled, one by one.

Millie got less than anyone. It was a laughable

sum of money to them, she knew, a final paternal snub. But it was more than enough, she thought, to buy her husband back.

When she got home she grinned, explaining the terms to Bill. She thought he'd be happy and she was surprised that he gave her the cool back of his spine when they crawled into bed.

Millie built her house. She bought a nice piece of land on the bone edge of the right part of town and picked out the architect herself. He was in fashion, respectable, but still young enough to be affordable for someone like her. Her house was huge, with room enough for grandchildren and a garden designed to her exact specifications; filled with flowering trees (whose blooms would last months), rose bushes, and a scuppernong arbour to attract birds. The magnolia (a two-foot sprout) was the first thing she planted. As a treat for Bill, she secreted an office for him in the attic where he could dissect engines to his heart's content and read his books on Civil War politics and the unjust terms of the Yankees' reconstruction in peace and quiet. She didn't mention it to anybody; if the lawyer found out her family could sue her for every cent she had. The money was meant entirely for her, and for her children, according to the contract. Bill could have no input.

The rest of the fortune she invested (money management seemed to run in her blood. She might have noticed this gift before if she'd had any chance to try it) and the trusts for her children exploded like myrtle blooms in April.

Time passed. Her mother died. Her siblings dropped off one by one without Millie ever seeing them. Bill retired and sold his business. He was careful to tell her that *that* money was his.

Their grandchildren grew. They went to school and then to universities – even the girls. Bill started getting quieter, drinking more. Millie spent hours, nearly whole days, tending her garden. She went outside the moment she finished cleaning the house, after Bill had risen and eaten his silent breakfast. She returned twice every day to prepare his lunch and dinner.

Bill never seemed to take an interest. He'd eat, watch Fox News on full volume (nodding his head whenever the host's tone of voice indicated, occasionally murmuring 'thass right' into his buttery grits), before slouching back up the stairs and into his office. Millie missed him, of course, but it was a hunger so deep that she hardly ever felt it. The boy she'd known had been missing for years.

She never criticised him in anything, never said a word to him when he ignored or struck her. She never batted an eye when he came home drunk at three in the morning, smelling of other flesh than hers. She was, in short, as good a wife as she'd been trained to be. She was obedient. She followed the law, in spirit and letter, and anyway her mate had been an excellent provider. They would have been able to retire, years ago, even without her inheritance.

When Bill put down his fork one day, dropped his greasy napkin on the polished tiles of her floor, and walked out into the sunset garden Millie was surprised, but she knew enough to stay silent. She watched him standing in the blooming centre of the yard, his hardened hands on the sharp jut of his hips, as he swivelled his head to take in her whole green world. After a few minutes, he came back inside without bothering to shut the screen door behind him (in a moment the kitchen hummed with mosquitoes) and smiled at her with his thin, sharp lips, saying, 'You've made it real pretty out there, Millie.' He laughed and lightly touched her shoulder on his way up the stairs.

Millie felt an old, familiar stirring in her loins and heart. Her cheeks lit up with rose petals as she scraped the plates into the trash and started cleaning up. They made love that night, for the first time in years, and although it took Bill a little while to get started (and next to no time to finish) the pleasure was enough.

Millie slept deeply, sweetly, and woke up late to an empty bed and the harsh whine of a chainsaw.

Wrapping her 1970s powder-blue robe around her shoulders, she hurtled downstairs, through the kitchen, and into the yard.

She saved two of the myrtles, but none of the roses. Bill was standing there in the sunshine, sap on his hands and a grin on his mouth. She'd never shouted at him before, hell she'd never even contradicted him. She shouted now. She struck his bony shoulders with her small hands.

It did no good.

Bill shut off the motor, wiped the jagged steel chain with his handkerchief, and walked into the garage. When he reached the door he laughed (his face was joyful) and turned to her saying, 'I'm quittin' cause I'm tired. You didn't have nothin' to do with it.' He opened the door, 'Oh sweet Lord I feel good. Better than I have in years.' Then he vanished into the dark.

The next day the last of the myrtles spilled their red crepe heads onto the lawn while Millie sat weeping and clutching her mug at the plastic-covered table. The scuppernongs went next, arbour and all, then the jasmine that had flowered along the fence. It was around this time that their eldest granddaughter called. She showed up late one afternoon with the black woman that Millie referred to as her 'good friend'. She wept, too, when she saw the yard but Ronnie hadn't raised her well (as if her lifestyle choice weren't proof enough of that) and she ran outside and screamed at her grandfather until the old man said things that whitened her face and made her clutch at her stomach. She left in a huff, leaning on her girlfriend's round shoulders.

The slaughter continued unabated, after that.

This morning will be the last morning, Millie knows. She's felt a little worse inside, every day, ever since this whole mess began. There's just the one tree standing up in the yard. Millie knows that the magnolia buds have acted on a promise that she's kept up every year, but which will no longer be fulfilled. There will be no new night-blooms this year. Only one moon will raise its head in her dead garden, and the only lemon scent will come out of the plastic bottle by the sink.

Millie's learned her place. In her guts, she always knew exactly how little she was worth, and where that place was. She'll keep the curtains down and spend more time in the kitchen.

But for now, she looks out, seeking the lovely, living gleam of white and green against the blackest trunk in all creation. She ignores the chainsaw, the branch-cutter, the stump-digger, the axe. She looks outside and thinks, 'Magnolia', willing the ugly, hairy buds to open early and picturing a long, impossible series of mornings spent out there in alternating pools of butter-light and sweet-scented shade.

Lledrith
Diana Powell

Bone.

In the beginning, he had chosen bone, loving it for its constancy.

'Look,' he told Menna, lifting the skull from the spuming pink scum into the light, 'how it comes to this. Boiling or desiccation, and this is what we are.'

She turned away.

So he surrounded himself with the bodies of birds and mammals found on the heights, brought home to be reduced, their superfluity dismissed. Whole skeletons – a fox, a hare, a giant buzzard, a miniscule wren; a basketful of skulls; scapulae, thigh, rib; the yawning jaw, with grinning teeth, of a fallen sheep – there were plenty of those. He coveted, too, those other parts that shared its intransigence. Tooth, beak and claw. Horn. And he saw rock as bone, the final essence of the mountain he lived on. Scrape away the skin and flesh – the grass, the earth – and there it was. Nothing else.

So he used these things to make his art, his sculptures – strange constructs, some small enough to hold in the palm of your hand, some so large they must

285

be worked in the open, and left where they stood. A totem pole of rock, strung about with necklaces of vertebrae and claws. A mangled, rusting harrow, daubed with rubbish gleaned from the hills – 'the detritus of man'.

'See what I am doing,' he said to Menna. 'Imagining an ancient tribe. A tribe from *here*.'

She shook her head, shrugged and went back to her washing.

His human skull was his favourite piece, made living with 'found' objects. He had coloured it with dyes from the plants in the meadows below – pink from diluted madder, mixed with yellow from gorse, to make a peachy skin tone. The hair was from sheep wool caught on the wire fences; the eyes were of blue glass, worn smooth by the pebbles at the bottom of the nearby stream.

'A fetish,' he explained, patiently. 'Ancient, to begin with, from an Amazonian tribe, altered to belong here.'

'Who would buy it?' she asked. 'Who would buy any of it? How will it pay the bills?'

He cradled the skull to his chest. How could he tell her he wouldn't sell it, anyway? He would never sell any of it.

But, still, there was something else he sought, yearning for it through his waking hours, even as he worked, breaking his concentration, spoiling the cunning of his hands. Not just a skull, but a complete skeleton, to be turned into a skeleton-bride, the maiden of the tribe. And now, every night as he lay with Menna, his dreams were full of it, too. In those dreams, he worked on the form, seeing each tiny detail of what he must do, every stage of the work mapped out in front of him, until there she was – the perfect final accomplishment. Sometimes, Menna, beside him, would turn towards him, put her arm around him, move in closer. But he would turn away. He had had enough of her now. He had had enough of flesh. He wanted more... or less. But how?

And then, when he woke one morning, it was there, pushing the dreams away, demanding attention at the front of his thoughts, as if he were being told. A story, vague and uncertain, at first, then becoming clearer. The mountain was full of such things. They were as much a part of it as the earth and the wind, the rock and the sky. They were as much a part of him as his Welsh accent and the hiraeth that had brought him back here. Only he had forgotten. Until now.

And, straight away, he knew where he must go. He must start at the village, where the tale began. So it was down first, then up, as he followed the words out between the houses, through the wood, and started climbing. He lost their scent when the post-and-wire fences ran out, and the bent hawthorn gave up its struggle, when there was nothing left but mountain.

But now it was obvious to him. He must go to where
the bone showed through, and the cynefnin of the
sheep surrendered to bare rock. Where the gnarled
grey knuckles of granite clung on between earth and
air. This is where she would be.

But… there was nothing there. He searched all
around, but where was there to search? No trees,
bushes, caves; no cairn or hollow. Just rock. Where was
there to hide, as she did in the tale, running to escape
her bridegroom's friends, and their wedding-day
prank? He knew it would be secret – otherwise, how
could they not have found her, looking for days,
weeks, their shouts growing louder, more desperate,
with each returning echo. But still, then and now, there
was nothing.

He found it by accident – or by design. A hint of
a crevice, the rock overlapping at the front, to deceive
the eye. It was no more than a black shadow,
beckoning her – and now him – inwards. So narrow
that he thought he would be unable to follow, though
wide enough for her, for she was little more than a girl.
Still, he must go, holding his breath and flesh in,
keeping the perfection of her finished form in his mind.
And sure enough, as his eyes grew used to the dark,
there she was, still waiting for her lover. Her hands
were resting on the rock above her, raised towards the
air, as if she were reaching for it, for safety. But she was
stuck fast by her foot trapped in a jagged slit, just as it

said in the story. Returned to the mountain forever. Bone to bone.

He was lucky. The aridity of the chasm had preserved her well, the same dryness that stopped the growth of all plant life above her. And it had sustained her purity, keeping her free from bacteria and fungi, leaving her white. White, as the bridal gown she was dressed in, except there was none of that left, now. Only bone.

He touched her, gently at first, running his finger along a rib, down the ulna, half afraid she would crumble to dust. She was old, and even he knew that bone was not infallible. But no, she had stayed strong. She had endured. Of course, she would come apart when he moved her, but it didn't matter. He would resurrect her, as he had in his dreams.

Soon, every part of her was in his bag, except for her foot. The foot that had been clamped tight in the rock, spelling her doom, and killing her. He tried to prise it free, just as she would have done, when there was still flesh on it. It should have been easier for him, left with only phalanges, metatarsals, talus, calcaneus. Calcaneus – the heel bone that had twisted and locked her into place. And, after all these years, it was still unmoving. He felt pity then, imagining her cries, with no one to hear, except the buzzards and the wind. Imagining her frantic pulling and twisting as she tried so desperately to free herself, to reach the fresh air, and return to her forlorn lover. A cruel death. Slow. All the more reason to make her whole again. All the more reason to take her home, where she could be amongst others of her own kind, where she would, at last, be safe.

Of course, he knew there would be questions from Menna. And complaints – she did little else now. And sure enough, as soon as he tipped the bag onto his workshop table, she was there, beside him, with her tutting, and huffing.

'Shouldn't we call the police?'

'What would they do? It was over a century ago?'

'How can you be sure?'

'Surely you can see how old it is? Can't you see that it's a woman, just like the story says? The wide breastbone and hips. The slim waist. And the foot – the foot makes it certain.'

'Still… it should be buried…'

'I am going to treat it with dignity. That is all the law requires.'

'It's not right…'

'It's…'

On and on and on.

'Where's supper?' he said. And when she went through the door into the kitchen, he locked it behind her.

It took him weeks to make her as he wanted. He had the plan in his head, and his dreams to guide him, but still the work was difficult, painstaking. She had come from the mountain, so he wanted to keep her that way – belonging to '*here*', like his other sculptures. Their goddess.

First, there was the task of putting the bones back together.

'Two hundred and six bones in an adult body,' he told Menna. 'Less, of course, because of the missing foot – the foot has a surprising amount of bones, twenty-six, in fact – but still, a lot.'

'Why don't you go and do some labouring down the village,' she offered in reply.

He bound the bones together with the wire from the fences, threading, looping, tying, till his fingers were raw and bleeding. For the colouring, it was the same as the skull – the dyes from the native plants; but, needing more, he asked Menna if she would collect some. 'Get them yourself! I'm having nothing to do with that thing!' There was sheep-wool again for the hair, combed and long this time, to show it as a girl. And green eyes, now, from slate he had found on a walk to the north. Green, with flecks of hazel.

Soon, all was done, except for the stump trailing into nothingness. It had been missing in his dreams, too. He wondered, then, if he should have tried harder to free the foot. And what was he to do now? Should he just leave it, or replace it with a replica carved from the hawthorn? In the end, he decided on something quite different, something symbolic. A boot. White leather, with a heel, and fancy lacing. Just the thing for a bride, found in a second-hand shop in the town. The only thing not of the mountain.

'There!' he said, the morning it was finished, though there was no one there to say it to. Menna was still sleeping. Perhaps he was saying it to the skeleton.

'There! You are perfect!'

He set her in the armchair he kept out there 'for contemplation', facing the kitchen door, so that she would greet anyone who entered. So that she would greet Menna.

'How can you?!' Menna shrieked the first time she saw her. 'It's horrible! It's not right! And what if anyone sees her? What will they think?'

'We say that she came from an anatomical supplier, that it was in the back of an antique shop, that I used to be a medical student – anything you like… that she is another example of my art.'

'Art! What art?'

He could have killed her then.

It was easier when she had left. When it was just the two of them. He brought Ffraid into the kitchen – for, yes, he gave her a name; it was simpler that way, easier than saying 'skeleton bride', or 'bone woman' – there was nothing more to it than that. He decided upon 'Ffraid', the Welsh for 'Bride'. It seemed the perfect choice.

He hung her from the meat hook in front of the hearth. Sometimes, she moved – in the draught of the open door, in the heat of the rising flames; sometimes, for no reason at all that he could see. Perhaps it was the shrinking of the cords that bound her. What else could it be… except, of course, he had used metal.

She watched him, as he made his tea, washed the mug, plate and spoon; watched, even, as he washed himself in the old zinc bath in front of the fire. Now and then, he talked to her. There was nothing wrong in that. It was no different from talking to yourself, or to a cat. Or to the stuffed owl that had hung there before her. She was a willing listener. Not like Menna, with her endless questions, her constant gibbering, and complaint. Her lack of understanding of his work. Of him.

Sometimes, she talked back – only a word or two, a word of comfort, or encouragement. It was no more than a sound, really, but still he was glad of it. One day – a day that had been particularly hard, with more bills coming, and no food in the larder – she put her hand on his shoulder. He supposed it was just that he had brushed against her, or that the draught had moved her in his direction. But still, it had been welcome.

It was then that he decided to give her new hair. The sheep wool had been a mistake; it made her look old. It fell out. So he replaced it with long, gold tresses. Like Menna's. He wrapped a shawl around her shoulders – one of Menna's, that she had left behind; she had left everything. Ffraid looked much better now.

Sometimes, as he was bathing, he would glance up, and see her green eyes staring down at him, lit by the glow of the flames. And the steam from the water would rise up around her, rounding her edges, softening the hardness of the bones, making the golden hair shimmer. And he would smile.

So that was how they lived – comfortable, you might say.

He liked to think she felt a sense of belonging, a feeling of what it was like to have her own home. She had never felt it before, having missed her marriage, by an hour or two, and lost her love. All those years in that cold, stone chamber; all those years alone. It was good for her to be warm and wanted. 'It's okay,' he told her. 'You're mine, now.' The words echoed round the room.

And yet, suddenly, she was not enough. Bone was not enough. He wanted more. Not flesh – he had had enough of that with Menna, and had discovered that he could do without it. But there was something else

missing. He had made nothing new for months – not
since he had finished his work on the skeleton, as if he
had been sucked dry by the effort. Indeed, there was an
emptiness, a hollowness in him, as if his bones, too,
had nothing between them.

He found himself getting cross with her. 'You're
in my way,' he might say, pushing past her, making
her spin. Or 'for God's sake, why can't you shut up?' It
was the same kind of thing he would tell Menna, when
she was nagging, or making him angry. But what had
Ffraid said? What had she done?

One day, when he had been sitting in his
workshop for hours, staring at his tools, at the carcass
of a raven he had found on the mountains a week ago,
unable to fashion the materials in front of him to even
the most basic form, unable, even, to think of what he
might want to do with the bird, he went back into the
kitchen, and yelled at her, and picked up the poker,
ready to strike her with it. She stared coldly at him
with her dead eyes. That's all they were – nothing else
but dead. He had been a fool to think otherwise. He
knew then what was missing.

He went back to the stories, picking over them,
in his mind, as he should be doing with the raven-
carcass in the flesh. He threw away the goblins and the
gwrach, the bwgans and the fairies, ignored the water
monster and Arthur and his knights. Even the white,
grey and green ladies – lovely as some of them were,
they were not what he craved. All were banished to the

furthest recesses of his memory, until he was left with one. A lledrith – 'fetch', he believed it was called in English; doppelganger, maybe, in stranger tongues. A ghost, but not a ghost, the spirit of someone still alive. A death omen, some said, but not in this telling – the story of two young wives, apart, but the same. And, as before, he knew where to go. But would she still be there; did the haunting continue year after year, for ever and ever, or happen only the once? And if she was, how would he capture her? There would be no hard bones, this time, nothing solid to grasp, pull and tear at. Just a spirit, which is what he wanted now.

In the end, it was easy. There she was, as the words had told him, on the drover's road, leading to the market in the big town. And yes, she was just as he imagined – like Menna had looked once upon a time, or the hanging woman had appeared, disguised by steam and flame. He watched her the next day, and the next, so that he was sure of her meaning. Each time, she came walking, leaving her husband behind.

'But how will you catch her?' Ffraid asked him that evening. 'After all, she's not a real ghost.' Perhaps he was asking himself.

'All I can do is try the old way – a candle in a jar, to draw and trap.' The figure above him just laughed.

And yet, when he left the jar in the darkness of the following evening, sure enough, he returned next morning to find it full of light. An incandescence, so powerful that he feared he would be blinded, so what else could it be but the essence of a ghost? Something else for his bag, but so much lighter this time, than one hundred and eighty human bones.

He took it home, and placed it on the kitchen table, still covered. Ffraid looked down and tutted. More and more now, she sounded just like Menna. She asked the same annoying questions, too.

'But won't it simply escape, through the walls, once you let it out? Isn't that what ghosts do?'

'You're the one who said she's not a real ghost. But the candle worked, didn't it? I'll try the same ways again.'

He drew a circle around the outside of the house, and walked around it, offering prayers and incantations found in an ancient book. Then he placed branches of rowan inside it, rowan for witches and evil spirits – why not a lledrith, too? For extra measure, he pinned psalms and verses from the Bible to the walls. And when all that was done, he worked his arm into the bag and opened the jar.

At first, she was still no more than a light. Yet, straight away, the glow spread, diminishing its brightness, so that there was no need for him to cover his eyes. Then, day by day, she took on substance and outline, until she had become the wraith of full-sized woman, fair and comely, just as he had wished. There and not there. Here, and somewhere else. Lledrith.

But yes, those first few weeks, she tried to get out. Perhaps she wanted to return to the place that she haunted, or to the house she lived in, and clung to, while her spirit roamed. Perhaps that was the way of the lledrith – he knew little about it. Maybe she was pining for her husband, for he was sure he could hear crying in the night. And one day, when he came in, she rushed at him, almost knocking him over, as she made for the open door. But the rowan, or the circle, or the strangeness of her surroundings, slammed into her fragile being, shattering her into a million screaming fragments, scattered about the room. She gathered herself back together, and slunk back in, and didn't try to escape again.

After that, the crying stopped, and she seemed to grow used to the kitchen, which was perhaps not so different from her own. Of course, he named her – like before, it was easier. Dwyn-wen. White fetch. Or something stolen. The Welsh saint of lovers – but that was just coincidence.

Now that she had settled, he was worried that Ffraid would be cross with him, for bringing another here – just like Menna hadn't liked *her* arrival. And yes, at first, she turned away when he came near, and fixed her cold eyes upon him, and stopped talking to him. It didn't matter, he had Dwynwen for company now.

But still, he didn't want to make Ffraid jealous. He wanted harmony in the household, he wanted to feel that comfort he had known, when Menna had first

come to him, and then Ffraid. The peace and
contentment that had been good for his art, and his
soul.

So he took her down from the hook, and placed
her in the alcove by the hearth. She fitted there snugly,
the two sides supporting her, making it look as if she
was leaning there, warming herself, maybe. He
thought it would make her feel less apart. After a
while, Dwynwen took to sitting near her. In the story,
he remembered now, she had been sitting by the fire,
sewing, when her husband left her to go to market,
then came across her on the track. Perhaps she liked to
be in the old place, feeling at home there. Or perhaps
she just needed the warmth. She was not a true ghost,
after all, and it was cold in the cottage.

And yes, after a while, Ffraid no longer glared at
him, or complained to him. In fact, she seemed to want
little to do with him now, but in a pleasant enough
way.

Sometimes, coming in, he would find Dwynwen
even closer to the skeleton, her head almost bowed into
her, as if they were talking. But, of course, how could
that be? Still, he was glad they were happy together,
that they were all happy together. Quiet and
comfortable, just as he had wanted. And, yes, his work
was improving, changing direction, and finding, he
believed, an emotion that had been missing before.

One night, he was woken by a sound.
Whispering, he thought. But it must be his imagination.

The old house made noises, the creaking of the boards, spiders scurrying in the plaster of the walls, mice scuttling in the attic. That's what it was, nothing more. Yet it was there the next night, and the next. Every night, then, so that his sleep was never full.

And once, coming down to get a glass of water, he thought he saw a movement, a rushing of light out between the bones of the skeleton. He rubbed his eyes. There were the two of them, in their usual places. It must have been no more than sleep.

Then he began to hear giggling. The staccato, mocking laughter of girls – a sound remembered from childhood and beyond. The girls in the schoolyard, gathered together in a corner, laughing and pointing at him; the girl-students in art college, looking at his work, and laughing. Just laughing. Every night it was there, together with the whispering – yes, it was most definitely whispering, not the old house, after all. Words reached him through the floorboards. Cruel words, black and hard. Like stones thrown at him. And sticks. He remembered his mother telling him the rhyme, when he would run home crying to her. But he had never believed it.

Sleep was hard now.

And poor sleep meant poor work. No work, before too long.

And when he went to eat, he would find there was no food there, even though he was certain the cupboard had been full before.

And he didn't want to bathe any more. He didn't want them to see him naked, to start their giggling again. Just like those other girls, all the girls before Menna.

In the kitchen, they would throw things at him, crockery, ornaments, books, so that soon he was battered and bruised.

He spent more and more time upstairs now, away from them. Starving, alone and cold.

He would get rid of them. He would rub out the circle, move the rowan, and open the door, and Dwynwen would simply go – back where she came from, where she wanted to be. Ffraid – he would cut the wire, turning her back into a pile of bones. And then he would take them up to the top of the mountain, and scatter them on all sides, down, down, below.

Soon, he would do it, as soon as he felt stronger.

'Do you hear me?' he shouted. 'You'll be gone soon. Both of you! Gone for good!'

When she first entered between Ffraid's bones, both felt the rightness of it – how much better they had felt -

and, for a while, it had been enough. And then, in time, they yearned for something more.

Flesh. Flesh was missing. They needed flesh.

They knew where to find it. Shreds of it, anyway, littering the workshop, waited to rot from the bones. They gathered together this and that, taking it back to the kitchen. But it was not enough. Somewhere, Ffraid said, they would find the other – the one who had lived here before, who had flesh aplenty… or used to. But that was outside, where they could not go, on account of the circle and the rowan. Besides, the cottage had become their home, now. No, they must find more inside. They needed more. And blood – blood would be useful. And skin, to keep them together always. Where would it be?

Bone. He knew now what it was to be bone. After all, there was little else left to him. They had taken it away, the meat of his body. And the heart, too. They had taken that. They had been gentle enough in the beginning, but soon there was pain. They looked at him, but there was no pity. The two of them, reaching into him, taking what they needed, to make them one.

And she stood there now… what was she? He couldn't say. He could say nothing. Nothing at all.

Three Poems
Kathy Miles

Red Kite

Above the cloisters of soil and shrub,
she hovers in her astonishing red,

wings scorching the air as she spools
across fields of sheaves and cut stubble.

Jackdaws spin like flecks of grey ash
girdle her with a jabber of black,

tugging the air with their loud complaint.
She tilts into the wind, her call a high frail

on the current, and her shadow falls across
the pond and the slow leat as she circles her heft,

a shawl of rain misting the hedges, the redshift
of her feathers quilled against the sun.

Above, a dissonance of stars, the suttee of day
fading into evening, moon unfolding its yellow eye.

Veteran
(i.m. Neil Tierney, 1913-2001)

Another day, and a coiled note of autumn,
the keen of rain on the glass.

My father, burly as a brown bear,
shambling down his garden,

planting his feet steadfast in the soil
as though doubtful of its firmness.

He has the cast of old scars printed on the yield
of his soul. Unable to forget the script of the past,

the unforgiving gristle of his dreams
sounding like gunfire on the cord of night.

He turns, pushes open the gate, and is surprised
by sun, weather, the amazing commonplace of things.

I think now of the truth of him,
the terrible load of memory.

How he carried it always like a sack of coal,
aching from its weight, unable to put it down.

Vanishing Point: Venice

Here, the slow decay of water,
shutters and crumbling stucco,
soft lap on stone in hard-oiled light.

Lucid shadows, fragile as ormer shells,
a pearl gauze locking chiaroscuro
onto peeling walls, doors hennaed by sun.

Lizards, pale against chipped brick,
scud down to damp glazed pavements,
the surge of tide across the square.

Vaporettos coast the Grand Canal
like Stations of the Cross: landing stages
bob wildly in their wake.

In the cemetery, the dead are slipping
into water, quietly over the centuries;
cypress sit in a root-wash of waves.

On Poveglia, ruins roofed with branches,
windows trellised by vine and bramble.
Peach-trees grow in bone-rich soil,

haunted by the souls of ashed bodies
from the plague-pits, the ghosts
of doctors in long beaked masks.

This hiraeth of water remembers
merchant fleets - galere da mercato -
the shallow draft of galleys, sleek hulls

slipping through the locks: silks,
dyes, cloves and gold, spilling
like sacks of gems on the harbour wall.
It remembers the vedutista scumbling
paint on canvas, the scribbled purl of ships,
black gondolas straining like stallions

on their ropes. Everything is mirror,
reflection, the sfumato of cloud twinned
in early morning haze on the lagoon.

A city built on stilts, poled into salt-marsh
on alder and larch. A slow dissolve.
The water's lapse, the vanishing point.

And one day it will belong to grebe,
to night heron and egret, to tern
and cormorant, the tender eucharist of light.

Sometimes There's God
Jon Boilard

The old man has a stroke some weeks after Harlan
Bovet's mother goes missing. Harlan hates his father
even more now that he's a fucking invalid. The emotion
was already there, but deep and buried, and now it has
bubbled to the surface. He visits because it's a pleasure to
watch him die. There's a Puerto Rican girlfriend
apparently from the old man's past who is nice enough
and cleans him up when he shits his pants, which is all
the time, as far as Harlan can tell. Her name is Lila. She
waits tables at the Howard Johnson's by the Greenfield
rotary, and she suddenly reappeared when Harlan's
mother disappeared. She wheels the old man around the
house with his oxygen tanks and takes over Harlan's old
bedroom. There's a stray cat living in the room next to
the garage where Harlan crashes sometimes when
Annabelle throws him out. His old man doesn't recognise
Harlan. Lila uses a paper towel to wipe spittle from his
chin.

> How is he, Harlan says.
> Good days and bad days.
> All right.
> Mostly like this, she says.

I don't know how you do it.

Some days I don't either.

I hear how he talks to you.

Yeah, and that's on the good days.

Harlan laughs. Lila is all right in his book. She gets him a can of Budweiser beer and she has a highball with a green olive stuck through with a toothpick. The old man simply stares out the window at the haze and into the pitch of night and drools some more.

He doesn't even know me any more, Harlan says.

No, he does.

Not that I'm complaining.

It just takes time to register.

If he knew it was me drinking his beer he'd be pissed, Harlan says.

Lila laughs. She asks him about Annabelle.

Oh, she's still around, he says.

And have you heard from your mother then.

Nah, he says. She's probably down to Florida.

Well, I cleaned up that room in case you need it.

Much obliged.

Clean sheets and everything.

All right.

The works.

Thanks.

Just in case. You still have your key.

Sure, he says. I have it somewhere.

Well, don't be a stranger.

I know.

He's your father after all.

Don't remind me.

It's Lila's turn to laugh again.

Harlan gives her a hug and she takes the empty can from him and disappears into the kitchen so he can have a moment with his father. A gurgle in the old man's throat. Harlan moves close so they're face-to-face and he looks for a trace of the mean old bastard he remembers but all that's left is a pathetic and empty human shell. He uses the back of his own sleeve to wipe white bile from his father's dry prune lips. Harlan is greased and feels one of his episodes coming on and so he naps in the chair for a couple hours. It feels good to be so completely alone.

He rides to the Ashfield Lake House and orders a Jack and Coke. There isn't much going on. He drinks three more and then takes his bike back down Route 116 and through the centre of town. He sees the woman in front of the Hot L, Nikki from the other night, who hired him to drill the dude at Joey D's. He pulls over and removes his helmet, and at first she doesn't recognise him. Then she smiles, drags on her cigarette, plays it cool like.

What you doing, he says.

I don't know.

Well, he says. Hop the fuck on. He gives her his extra helmet and she hops on, flicking her cigarette into the street. Annabelle is in the back of his mind. Where to, he says.

Wherever.

They go down the mountain and cross the river to Mike's Westview. Harlan puts the bike out back beside a pile of lumber. They go inside and lean against the high bar, order some drinks.

So the other night, she says.

Yeah.

That's what you do.

What's that now.

The thing you did for me.

What about it.

Well, she says. Is that what you do.

I do it sometimes.

You give out beatings for a living.

That wasn't a beating.

What do you call it then.

I don't call it nothing.

Nikki laughs and sips her drink and looks at Harlan.

Anyhow, she says. He's up to his old tricks again.

That same guy you mean. Did he hit you.

Worse than that he kicked me out.

You're saying that's worse than getting hit.

In a college town it is, she says. You try to find an apartment in September.

But you really thought he'd let you stay after that.

I don't know.

After I said your name so he knew it was you sent me.

I guess I didn't know.

Right.

Or think it through.

Harlan looks at her.

He used to love me, she says after a minute.

I bet.

Maybe it was a test.

So.

Yeah exactly, she says. So fucking what.

Nikki finishes her cheap version of a cosmopolitan and they go to Harlan's parents' garage and sit in the spare room and smoke a joint. He's drunk enough he tells her all about Annabelle and describes her as the love of his life, but Nikki doesn't give a shit about that. They kiss and she uses her hand on him and then she stands up and takes her clothes off. He watches. Then he stands up and gets undressed too and she turns around and grabs the kitchenette sink and puts him deep inside her. They bump against each other like that for a while.

Then, lying on the mattress to catch their breaths, they hear Harlan's father upstairs cursing. It sounds like he's throwing things and flipping furniture over and Harlan laughs. He tells her about his old man, the history there. He calls her Darling Nikki after the song by Prince.

So he's just dying up there, she says.

Dying or already dead.

Sounds like he's got some life left in him.

Maybe hate keeps him going.

Hate.

He had enough of that I seem to recall, Harlan says.

Darling Nikki puts her head on his chest. So what do we do now.

Just lay here for a minute and rest and be real fucking quiet.

He puts his finger to his lips. Shhhhhhh, he says.

I mean after that, she says.

After that you'll do what you do, he says. And I'll do what I do.

Darling Nikki likes the way that sounds, prefers being the other woman. Later she tells him she's crashing at a friend's house in Whately so that's where he drops her. He doesn't mind at all. There is a little dog barking out front and she calls him Nanook. He's a Jack Terrier. She tells Harlan that Nanook caught a squirrel the other day and whipped it around like they do and broke its neck. Then she doesn't know if she should kiss him goodbye or hug him or maybe nothing at all so she just stands there and he rides off without saying anything.

Annabelle takes Harlan up north to clear his head. She says the fresh air will do him good. They climb Mount Washington and sleep in a tent. They find a gentle bend in a river where they can swim naked and nobody else is around. Everywhere else there are busloads of people.

She isn't much for roughing it, so it's good they have access to bathrooms with running water and big metal lock boxes that are bear proof. The second night they eat pizza in some one-horse town and Harlan drinks three pitchers of beer until they won't sell him any more and close the window on him. It's mostly college students working there and they don't know what to make of the man with the scars and the cauliflower ears and the beautiful young woman.

This must be a great job, Harlan says. For somebody in their twenties.

Walking back to their tent to go to sleep there are puddles from a storm that had just missed them. Harlan splashes Annabelle to try to make her laugh but she isn't having any of it. Harlan splashes and splashes until some random guy tells him he got his wife wet. Harlan puts on doll eyes and tells dude to fuck off. Annabelle sees where it's going so she wraps him up and practically drags him away.

He could've asked nice but he was doing that for his wife, he says. Showing her how big and brave he is in his LL Bean camping outfit right out of the catalogue. Then Harlan lets Annabelle think she saved him even though the truth of the matter is he was just too lazy to whip the guy's butt at that particular moment.

She tells him she was embarrassed and she won't let up on him. Then Harlan sings to her, trying to be funny, and eventually gets impatient and somewhat rough. He's still feeling playful so he makes wolf or coyote sounds until she shushes him several times and people in the nearby tents ask him to shut the Christ up after a while.

Harlan closes his eyes.

When he opens them Annabelle tells him he ruined everything. It's morning now. He doesn't remember, which is a result of the booze and the drugs and all those years of fighting. She tells him she cried all night long and that his snoring was worse than ever. He feels like shit about it, and he sits on a set of wooden steps and smokes and campers are giving him looks, but of course nobody dares say anything.

They walk in a meadow and there's too much sun for Harlan so he sits on a dead tree in the shade until she wakes him, tells him that he's killing himself and Harlan thinks maybe she's right. She wants him to quit scrapping and he wants her to quit stripping but then what would they do. Back on the bike he feels better, like an old-time cowboy in that setting and with her holding on tightly to him, her warm breath on the back of his neck when they stop to look at a pair of deer that are lost. It's a deep-chested buck and a white-nosed doe and in a rare moment of reflection Harlan says, Look, it's me and you. Annabelle laughs and that's the first sign of something good in a long while.

Kerosene Dream is playing at the Seven O's. Annabelle is wearing a short skirt for the occasion and at intermission Bart D'Armand sits with them backstage, and they smoke

a joint and talk about back in the day, bareknuckling at
the scrapyard. Bart was tough back then but lacked killer
instinct and that was before he had started the band.
Then Bart has to finish his set but Harlan and Annabelle
stay behind, sitting on a speaker case. They can hear the
music, Bart singing about his old Country Squire. Harlan
gets on his knees and uses his mouth on her.

Afterward it takes Annabelle a few minutes to
catch her breath.

Oh my God, she finally says.

Don't drag him into this.

I need a cigarette.

Harlan lights two and hands one to Annabelle.

I don't know how you do that, she says through a
smoke ring.

Harlan laughs.

I'm serious, she says. That's something else, boy.

Harlan laughs again and holds her hand and they
walk back out into the bar area and order a couple more
drinks. He can still taste her, ripe cantaloupe. Then it's
her third drink and that puts her past her limit lately and
she's fading fast. After Bart does his last song, Harlan
takes her home. She isn't keen on the idea of him staying
out without her but she's too tired to argue, but she
makes him promise to keep it in his pants.

Harlan meets Tim Looney at the Filling Station.

They eat cheeseburgers and French fries and drink
chocolate frappes.

Tim clears his throat. So listen, he says. Here's the thing.

Tim tells Harlan about the trouble with his asshole brother trying to scam his elderly parents out of their house in Bucktown, and now maybe even trying to poison them to get his filthy mitts on his inheritance. How there's no talking to the guy and Tim is at his wits' end.

Harlan looks at him when he's done talking.

I need some help, Tim speaks up. And I heard some shit about what you do.

Well, I don't know what you heard.

That maybe you could talk to him.

You just said there's no talking.

I don't know what else to do, Tim says. Where else to go.

Just get it straight what you want to happen besides talking and let me know.

Tim covers dinner and Harlan shakes his hand and unfurls his plastic poncho. It's raining, coming at him sideways. Harlan considers waiting it out but he doesn't know how long it will be.

He calls Sonny from the payphone in the diner.

Yeah.

Sonny.

Where you at, Sonny says.

Just ate at the Station.

Hey, somebody here wants to say hello.

There's a woman's voice. Harlan doesn't recognise her at first. She's teasing him, calling him the Boogie Man, Franklin County Badass, Southpaw. He plays along until he figures it out. It's Sherry. Her twin Mary is in the background wrestling around with Sonny, it sounds like.

Well, shit, he says.

Harlan could use some company, a drink.

Come over and see us, Sherry says. Why don't you.

You read my mind. See you soon.

The wind tilts the Harley and makes it hard to handle on the slick blacktop so Harlan takes it slow to Sonny's one-room shithole on Main Street in Turner's Falls, right above Waters and Sons Plumbing. Then Mary is sitting on Sonny's lap and Sherry is mixing up a cocktail.

Look what the cat dragged in, Sonny says.

He has coke in his new handlebar moustache that he calls the Firefighter Special.

Hey, Harlan says.

You're soaked, Sherry says.

Yeah, it's coming down good now.

Sherry hands him a drink and he takes a long tug off of it.

Ahhhhh.

Well, let's get you out of those wet clothes, she says. Before you catch your death.

She takes his hand and leads him to the small bedroom in back. Sonny laughs and Mary does too.

Harlan can hear them chopping up some more blow.
Sherry undresses Harlan and then she gets undressed too
so they can take a hot shower together. The water on his
skin is like a million bee stings. She looks good with her
black hair wet. He grabs it like a ponytail behind her
head and pulls back and uses his mouth on her neck and
tits. Then he picks her up and carries her to Sonny's bed,
which smells like fast food, and eventually they end up
sweaty and sticking to each other with whatever didn't
end up inside her.

Harlan gets a headache and closes his eyes.

Then the sun comes up.

There's a knock on the door. It's Mary.

Sherry, she says.

Huh.

Get up girl we got to go. But take some shit first.

Um hmm.

Check he's got a watch.

Sherry pulls herself away from Harlan, unsticks
herself from him, and gets dressed. He's sound asleep.
She pulls the sheet over him and kisses him on the
forehead and then she goes through his wallet as well as
the pockets of his pants and jacket. Several hours later
Sonny wakes up and finds Harlan in his bed. It takes him
a few minutes to remember the events of the night before.
Harlan opens his eyes and sees Sonny sitting on the edge
of the mattress.

Jesus fucking Christ, Harlan says. Where am I.

You're in my bed.

Oh shit. Them girls are poison, Harlan says. I bet they cleaned us out.

They always do.

Harlan laughs. Sonny laughs too. Harlan gets up and looks around for his clothes that are balled up and still wet and now smell of mildew like and he gets dressed. It's noon and Annabelle is going to be pissed because he was supposed to work on the Z28. He was supposed to keep it in his pants last night. He stands in the bathroom and looks at his bad reflection in the mirror and thinks about Annabelle. Feeling guilty, he rubs one off to her image in his mind. Then he does a couple lines with Sonny and drinks cold orange juice right from the container.

Annabelle wants to know where he's been. More than that, who he's been with.

I can smell that dirty pussy on you, she says.

He looks at her.

Don't think I can't, she says.

She doesn't like being kept in the dark any more. She feels that their relationship has progressed beyond that point and if he can't get a handle on his appetite then their plan is not going to work.

Harlan listens patiently and rolls a cigarette around on his bottom lip but he doesn't light it because the landlord has a rule about smoking. All his clothes and shit are stuffed into a garbage bag and sitting by the front door. Annabelle has given him an ultimatum.

Yeah, but what about you and that Greek piece of shit, Harlan says.

That's just a money thing, Annabelle says. That's just work.

Harlan spits on the floor when she says it.

Bullshit, he says.

Get the fuck out, she says. Then she starts crying. Get your shit together or we're through, she says. Though the Greek's offer is sounding better to her every fucking day.

Harlan lets her cry a few minutes. He puts his hand on her shoulder and she gets chills and she backs away from him and throws her cup. It misses but hot coffee splashes on his leg.

Fuck, he says.

Get the fuck out.

That hurt.

You don't know hurt, she says. You son of a bitch.

Harlan grabs his gear. On the bright side this is one way of getting out of spending his afternoon under the hood of her car. His bike won't start and she's watching from the dining room window and so Harlan rolls down the hill out of her line of vision until the bike will turn over. He sits there in idle for a little while, collecting his thoughts, coming up with a plan. Then a couple hours later Lila isn't surprised to see him. She's taking out the trash and he helps her.

How long you gone to stay for this time, she says.

I don't know.

Come up for a beer when you're settled.

All right then.

Still amped from last night's coke he goes upstairs for that beer. His old man is in white boxer shorts that are stained and a white T-shirt that has yellow rings under the arms and around the neck. From his bed he's fighting Lila over something and Harlan helps get him under control.

After a while the old man settles down.

Thanks for that, she says. He doesn't have much left.

That makes your job easier.

She gets him a cold beer and they don't talk and Harlan's head hurts, and he's happy to just sit there holding Lila's hand, with his eyes closed, listening to his father's laboured breathing.

On Tuesday Annabelle comes by with more of his personals.

Can we talk.

About what.

About us, she says. About our plan to fuck off out of here. You still think we can do it.

Yeah, he says.

But you got to stop with the strange pussy, she says. I just don't know what to do sometimes.

I know. But what about the fucking Greek.

Jesus. How much have you had to drink already.

Not enough.

Well, she says. So this is just a break then. A short break so you can get your mind right about our future.

Our future. All right.

He doesn't want to take a break. He imagines that fat bastard climbing on top of Annabelle, and he in the next instant he imagines snapping his neck like a twig. Then he shuts his eyes and just sits there on the edge of his mattress. She wants something more from him than he is able to give, it seems. That's what it boils down to from his perspective. Annabelle stares at him and shakes her head from side-to-side. Then they can hear his old man upstairs going into a rant. Lila's voice is calming at first but soon enough she's drowned out by a stream of booming obscenities. Annabelle never stops looking at Harlan and he finishes his drink and sucks on an ice cube and avoids her eyes. She eventually gets up and sighs and leaves.

There's a black and white television hooked up to power in the garage by an orange extension cord that runs through the window in the kitchenette. Harlan watches reruns of *The Price is Right*. The reception is not so good. He only barely gets three of the local channels.

Some yahoos race old American cars down South Main. Harlan likes the way the chrome bumpers look. He stands under a tree and watches them go up the hill. Then here comes the police with the lights and sirens and everything. It looks like Westy behind the wheel and Harlan figures those knuckleheads are lucky because he is one of the good ones at least. Then Sonny rolls up in his El Camino just out of the shop. He's listening to metal and it's cranked up really fucking loud. Harlan flicks his cigarette butt into a pothole in the street and gets in.

Turn that shit down already, he says.

If it's too loud then you're too old.

Fuck you.

Sonny turns it down a little and then he continues to sing along and drum the steering wheel. Harlan puts his arm out the window and his head back against the sun-warmed vinyl seat.

So where in fuck we going, he says.

There's this thing I heard about. But first we got to meet Spider.

Ah that fucking guy. It sounds complicated already.

Nah.

Harlan doesn't like it when things get too complicated. He needs a drink. He knows there's always a half pint of Jim Beam in a speaker hole and he takes a couple healthy pulls from it and hands it to Sonny. Then they park in the dirt lot of the abandoned shoe factory.

They said for us to go right in, Sonny says.

Who's they, Harlan says. You said Spider.

Sonny lifts the plastic that's hanging over a side entrance and holds it up for Harlan. Come on, Sonny says again.

Harlan goes in first and Sonny follows and it takes a minute or two for their eyes to adjust. Rats scurry around and you can hear them in the shadows.

Then somebody pats them down, tells them to put their arms up, to spread their feet apart.

This is the one you told me about, another voice says.

Sonny puts his hand on Harlan's shoulder. Yeah that's right, Sonny says. This here is my man.

And together you can do this thing.

Sure we can do it.

I want to hear your friend say it.

Harlan can see now and he takes it all in. He doesn't say anything.

Cat got your tongue.

He looks at Spider who's leaning against a doorframe.

I'm not a talker, Harlan says. That's what he does.

He nods toward Sonny.

I see, Spider says.

Harlan spits into the dust at his feet and eyeballs the bodyguard who is still looming, looking to get smacked.

Let's go, Harlan says. I don't like this one bit.

He pushes Sonny back out the way they came and Spider doesn't say anything.

Those are bad people there, Harlan says when they reach the car.

No shit.

I don't know, man. But go ahead and break it down for me.

You fight a guy or two. Five grand if you win.

Harlan looks out the window at nothing and whistles.

That's a lot of fucking scratch, he says. A guy or two, huh.

That's right. Like tournament style.

What guys.

His boys. He brings them in from the city.

Where and when.

He says we can pick a location. The weekend.

Jesus Christ.

With that kind of bread you can steal Annabelle away from that Greek fucking nigger.

Yeah, well, I guess that's the thing.

Darling Nikki isn't at her place but her roommate lets him wait inside. They smoke a blunt. Her name is Celia. She's a bohemian little thing. After an hour Nikki comes home and looks excited to see Harlan. She hugs him and sits on his lap and Celia rolls another one. They all three watch television and he rubs Darling Nikki's back and shoulders. Celia falls asleep on the floor with her mouth open and Harlan covers her with a blanket.

You're so nice, Darling Nikki says.

That's just a front.

Well your back's nice too.

Harlan laughs. He likes that she can make him laugh. Annabelle makes him laugh or at least she could when they started out but now she has put him on a break. Whatever that means.

Nikki tells him Joe isn't coming around so much any more. He seems to be getting the hint, she says. And she has a line on a duplex in Greenfield. It's a good place for her right now.

I'm in a good place, she says. And I have you to thank.

Well, go ahead and thank me already.

She works him from the outside of his pants with her hand. Then she unzips his fly and leads him like that to her room. Her dog is sleeping on a pillow on the floor and he looks up. Harlan makes a comment about performance anxiety in front of an audience and Darling Nikki laughs and shoos Nanook from the room and locks her door.

My poor baby, she says.

Him or me.

Him, because you're about to be all right.

She gets on her knees and undoes his pants and he watches the top of her head move up and down for several minutes until he finally relaxes and she even stays down there so that there isn't a mess of any kind. She looks up at him and then lets go his ass cheeks.

Where'd you learn that, he says.

Some things you don't need to learn.

Is that right.

Yeah you just know.

All right then.

Like you with the fights, she says, standing. Just comes natural.

Then she pushes him playfully back onto the twin mattress that she uses. It doesn't have a box spring. She catches him by surprise and he actually does lose his balance. He struggles through a brief bout with vertigo.

Not so tough now, she says.

Never said I was.

No you didn't, she says. But everybody else did.

Lila is outside having a smoke and Harlan bums one off of her. She can't smoke inside because of the oxygen tanks. They joke about what a mess that would make and Harlan even pictures it in his mind. Together they watch the full moon rise round and perfect. It's that curious time of day when the sun and the moon are in the sky at the same time. That nothing time caught between day and night. Not quite one or the other. Harlan's favourite part of the day, in fact.

A blood red sunset is draped over Mount Toby.

I had to call the volunteers the other day, she says. Everything just stopped. His heart and everything. He wasn't even breathing.

So that was it.

Maybe, Lila says. Almost.

Harlan looks at his old man.

I panicked, she says. I called Boho and the fire truck came, she says.

They generally do. Harlan looks at Lila and she looks away from him.

They brought him back like but took him to Cooley Dick to make sure, she says.

Should've just let him go like that, Harlan says. He doesn't mean to upset her but she cries just the same. I mean that wouldn't be too bad a way to go, he says.

I thought of that afterward. Of you. I knew you'd say that, she says. I looked for you downstairs.

I was out.

You were out, she says. You're always out. So they kept him overnight for observation, she says. I just got him back.

How is he now.

Same as always.

Harlan can smell his father. Lila cries some more. Harlan just stands there and lets her get it all out.

Bitch gives him warts and he's not even sure which one. A small doctor with an Indian accent and delicate brown hands freezes them off Harlan's pecker. He's going to quit all the others, Dirty Martini and Sally and Nikki whatever else pussy gets thrown his way. This is a decision Harlan has now made. He doesn't need it any more. It's become a hassle more than anything, and Annabelle wants to escape with him – that's how she termed it. Escape to Vermont or New Hampshire or where-the-fuck-ever. Escape from the fighting and the stripping and the whoring.

We're both whores, she'd said to him one time when they were just starting out together. And so how did we end up like this, she'd said.

How could we not, was all he could think.

But they've each managed to save a bit of scratch although he doesn't know what else he'd do once they got there, wherever. He figures he could get a job doing roadwork if there are any such jobs left.

I don't want to go somewhere new and do the same shit, he said.

Yeah, I'm done with this wrong life, too, she said.

She said it like she meant it but Harlan wasn't convinced they could either one of them pull it off. Even back then it had seemed like a fucking pipe dream. And now they're on a break.

He calls her on the phone.

Anyhow, he says.

So anyhow I'm going a for a few days, she said. It's no big deal.

The Greek takes Annabelle to Atlantic City. They stay at the Trump Towers and he plays blackjack until five in the morning. Annabelle gets bored and wanders around the casino, people watching. When they meet back at the room she's hammered and says he can do whatever he wants as long as he hurries. But what he wants is for her to use toys on herself while he squeezes his own juice

out. It doesn't take long. The next day she drinks
watered-down Mai Tais by the shitty little pool. There's a
group of professional bowlers lounging on the cement
deck. They try to get her attention but she's good at
ignoring drunk rednecks. Finally one gets up the balls to
approach her, and he's all right, but she tells him to fuck
off and so he does. His buddies laugh at him and
speculate aloud about her sexual preferences. She shuts
her eyes and tunes out all the noise and she thinks about
Harlan. He said he was going to kill the fucking Greek.

She believes that he will, that he can, but she is
more worried for him than for the other one.

He'd do it for sure if he knew she was with him
right now.

She shouldn't have mentioned the casino trip to
Harlan. She saw it has her chance to get away and think.
And she doesn't blame Harlan for being pissed, but she
had explained that there are some definite pluses to what
the Greek has put on the table; she'll be living in a nice
pad rent free so she can stop dancing for money and
focus on her poetry, for example. And the Greek's
various connections in the printing industry might be
able to help get her work published. These are the things
he has promised her. The downside of course is that he is
a disgusting pig and she's going to have to let him ravage
her a couple times a week. But she's been there before.
She can handle that. There's a place she goes inside her
head where nobody can touch her. She'd learned about
that special place as a young girl and can transport

herself there with the blink of an eye. But Harlan can't stand the thought of her being with another man like that. It drives him crazy.

We can still be together, she'd said.

He'll never even know, she'd said. Nothing will ever change between us.

But they both know that is a huge crock of shit.

Harlan's hands are hard as marble. He hits the dude's jaw so square that it feels like a bag of sand. Sonny cheers. Spider from the shoe factory and his bodyguard are there to watch, even though they don't usually get many spectators. He nods in approval but Harlan ignores him. It's the last one of the night and Sonny collects the money from everybody. Then he speaks to Spider but Harlan doesn't hear what they are saying, doesn't even want to know. He puts a clean T-shirt on and drinks a shot of warm whiskey. He sits on an old stool that is peeling paint.

He coughs blood.

Sonny gives him most of the money. That's the deal. Nice work, Sonny says. Hey, our friend was impressed.

Your fucking friend.

Whatever.

Harlan spits more blood and puts his head in his hands. He feels around his mouth with his tongue for a loose tooth. He spits it on the cement floor.

That night Annabelle stops by his father's place and says she wants him back.

I thought we were on break. You and the Greek and whatnot.

Fuck that, she says. I miss you.

Lila snorts. She's sitting on Harlan's bed with him. She'd brought him aspirin and orange juice and he's drinking it. Annabelle looks at Lila and dismisses her with a wave of her hand like to call her a skanky old bitch.

Well, she says to Harlan.

Well what.

You coming or what.

Where in fuck you been.

I went to Atlantic City with him. You remember.

You can't just waltz in here with his cock on your breath.

Annabelle can't believe what she's hearing. She'd convinced herself that Harlan had been pining away for her. She looks at Harlan and at Lila, then back at Harlan. A light bulb goes on in her head.

She has convinced herself of something else now.

You got to be shitting me, she says. Are you banging your father's ass wiper.

Jesus fucking Christ, Harlan says.

Lila snorts again and drinks her orange juice in three gulps. There's something else in there too that gets her through the day, most days anyhow.

That's it, Annabelle says. He's dying up there and you're fucking this washed up bitch, she says. Splitting his social security probably.

Lila stands up.

You always said that's all she was after, Annabelle says.

Lila balls up her little hand and throws it at Annabelle. It hits her in the face and takes her completely by surprise but doesn't do much damage at all.

Harlan gets up and bum rushes Annabelle before she can react. He practically carries her to her Z28, puts her inside. Get the fuck out of here, he says.

You cocksucker. I'm with the fucking Greek then.

As soon as she says it Harlan wants to hit somebody. It hurts to hear those words. The hell you are, he says.

She starts the engine and pops the clutch and has to start it again. Then Harlan watches until she's around the corner and he can't hear her grinding the Z28's gears anymore.

Lila is crying again inside.

Sorry about that, he says.

Oh, that's not on you, she says. I never did like that one.

Yeah.

It's not the money, you know. I don't want you to think that's what it is, she says. The only thing.

I know.

Did you really say that.

Well, I don't mean half what I say.

I mean it does help, she says. The cheques. I won't lie. It helps me some days when he's really awful, she says. To think about it.

All right, Harlan says. You don't have to explain nothing, I know how the world works.

I didn't even know about it at first, she says. That he even had a pot to piss in. Then when I found out he was already in such bad shape.

Come here. He hugs Lila as best he can and she shivers against him.

It wouldn't be so bad would it, she says.

What's that now, he says.

You and me.

Ah, he says, looking over her head out the window. He has never seen the sky so fucking blue. Sometimes there's God, he thinks, as a swarm of black crows alights just beyond the grain silo in the field across the way and other kinds of birds sit on a telephone wire that alternatively stretches and sags above Route 5. Harlan doesn't even want his old man's money. Lila can have it all. The house and the money and every-fucking-thing. He figures she deserves it. She's the one who has kept him out of the hospital or the nursing home or the graveyard. She's the one who has taken all the abuse, replacing his mother. Harlan truly likes Lila and never really thought that she was just in it for the cheques.

Mary asks Sonny for some nose candy.
Nobody calls it that any more, he says.
Whatever, she says. You know what I mean.
The great white snake, he smartasses.
Let's chase the great white snake then.
What do I get in return.
What do you want.
Sonny laughs his laugh because she knows exactly what he wants.
There's a ziplock bag in his sock drawer and he sets up a couple fat lines for her on the glass top of his coffee table. She uses a credit card to straighten them out and then hoovers them up her nose.
Where's your sister at.
What you want with her.
Nothing. I'm just asking.
We're not talking right now, Mary says. That bitch has mental problems, she says.
Sonny takes a couple quick toots just to be sociable. I'm supposed to meet Harlan, he says. Want to come, he asks.
Where.
The Bloody Brook.
That fucking place.
Yeah. I know.

All right.

Mary sits right up against him in the car, like they're going for couple of the year. It feels good to him when she does that.

This is like high school music, she says. What is this shit.

Creedence Clearwater.

Jesus Christ, she says. That's right.

Sonny opens the glovebox and fumbles around with some tapes. Mary takes them from him and looks them over and snickers. She looks at one and then drops it on the floor and then does the same with the next. Then she starts fooling with the radio dial, cruising the airwaves for something good.

Boy, you are out of touch, she says.

There's nothing wrong with those, he says. And you better pick them up.

She picks up the cassettes and puts them back carefully. I'm just saying, she says. That shit's old as fuck.

She knows he's in a bad way now and so she rubs his leg until he relaxes and then she puts on a station he likes. Sonny shakes his head, enjoys the way she's grooving in her seat. Then they're out in the street and Sonny hits her. But it isn't that hard and it won't even leave a mark. In his mind, the problem is that she's a fucking drama queen. He considers it more of a love tap than anything but she's screaming bloody murder. And of course he has to shut her up. It isn't like she hasn't been touched like that before. It isn't a new thing to her, getting knocked around a bit. So Sonny doesn't understand why she's getting all excited. When she finally calms down he tries to help her stand up but she just stays huddled against the kerb, sobbing.

He looks around to make sure nobody's being nosy.

And keep your trap shut about this, he says.

Fuck you.

Sonny can't believe how disrespectful she still is. He pulls his leg back to give her a good one in the ribcage and she balls up, and lucky for her he changes his mind at the last second.

You bring it on yourself with that mouth of yours, he says.

He gets two beers from a cooler in the back of the El Camino and pops them open and offers one to her. She won't even look at him. He drinks his and then he drinks hers too. He looks at her again. Mary looks up from what is now a sitting position and keeps quiet.

See, now that's better, he says.

Mary sniffles.

Sometimes you just got to know when to shut the hell up, girl.

Sonny puts seven ice cubes from the cooler in the ziplock bag he'd used for coke and he scoops Mary up off the street. She makes him so angry sometimes. The way she laughs at him isn't like he's in on the joke at all and that's almost always what pushes him over the edge.

You just need to check yourself, is all.

She looks at him this time and stays looking at him for a long time. She half smiles.

Fuck you, she says.

But he does love her spunk. She's a little spitfire. You're going to be all right, he says.

She's in a certain amount of pain and he hates to see that but he also knows deep in his heart that there are some hard lessons that have to be taught. He tells her about these lessons and how it's good for her in the long run. She moans, puts her head on him.

It's about respect and it's about knowing your place.

She nods her head up and down and he strokes her dark hair.

I hate when you make me get like that, he says. When you make me do like that.

I'm sorry, she says.

I don't know why you do that, he says.

She apologises again and he cradles her just like he might a baby or a small child and she wonders if he'll be a good daddy someday.

Spider is connected. That's what Sonny says when he meets Harlan at the Bloody Brook. No shit, Sherlock, Harlan says back. Sonny is thinking maybe he can help with the Greek. But the truth of the matter is Sonny has troubles of his own where he could use a boost. In debt up to his eyeballs. There were some ventures that hadn't proved as successful as he had hoped. The comic book store. The sandwich place. The coffee shop in Greenfield. He always has good ideas and he has balls enough to get things going but his problem is that he isn't a finisher. He's had a good run on the horses, though, and he plays poker at the Polish Club most Friday nights and he has the backwoods fight scene working pretty good. But never gets his head above water.

Sonny meets with Spider. He doesn't bring Harlan along because he's being such a wet blanket about the whole damn thing. They drink coffee at the pharmacy.

You play, Spider says, indicating the chess board on a nearby table, and when Sonny says he doesn't Spider asks why not.

I don't know. I'm too impatient, I guess.

It's a wonderful game, Spider tells him. Not unlike fighting.

But it's so fucking boring.

It's strategy. For both, it's strategy that wins.

Sonny thinks he's crazy but he doesn't mind crazy much. Spider then explains that there are serious consequences if they back out now. Once the ball is rolling and expectations are set.

Got it, Sonny says.

There's lots of details, Spider says.

Sonny is happy and relieved to not have to worry about the details.

*

Harlan is nowhere to be found. Sonny checks his old man's house and the Conway Inn and Mike's Westview, where he likes to go sometimes when it isn't too crowded with all the damn college kids. He even takes a ride into Turner's Falls to see if he's with Annabelle.

Why would he be here, she says.

I don't know, Sonny says. Why fucking not.

Annabelle's making coffee and invites him in for some. He follows her to the kitchen. She isn't wearing much, just an old T-shirt and a pair of pink cotton underpants that are going up her butt. She uses a finger to pick them out while she pours him a cup with the other hand and he watches and she catches him looking. She smiles at him, and Sonny sure knows what she's thinking, what she's up to here, and that is simply out of the question. Not that he would mind. To her it would be a sweet form of revenge perhaps, but to him it would be the same as suicide.

Well, she says. He doesn't stay here any more.

That's what I heard.

She looks at him. What else did you hear.

Her voice has turned bitter and he knows he has to walk on those eggshells now. Just that you were taking a break.

My ass, she says. That motherfucker is two timing me.

Sonny laughs and the steam of the coffee sooths the skin of his face where he shaved.

What's funny, Annabelle says.

He shakes his head at himself for being so stupid. Nothing, he says. Nothing's funny. He's nuts about you is all.

Well, she says. He has a different way of showing it.

Yeah, you know how he is.

They drink their coffees and she stands even closer to him now.

Look at me, she says.

It takes everything in him to not look at her.

What are you scared of, she says. She puts her empty cup down and stands right up against him. She runs her hand up his leg and she can feel how excited he is. Maybe scared's not the word, she says.

Sonny finishes his drink and gently pushes her away from him but she holds his arm.

Come on, Sonny, she says. I see how you look at me.

Looking's one thing, he says.

She takes his hand and places it on her and she pushes her pelvic bone against him.

Are we gone to do this, she says, or what.

He keeps his hand there for a little while. Yeah, he sure as shit knows what she's up to here. He's tempted but he considers the consequences and whether or not it would be worth it. He's on the fence now and lucky for him the phone rings and breaks him out of her trance.

Annabelle goes to the phone.

Yeah hello, she says.

Sonny puts his mug on the counter.

Oh hey, she says. The fuck you want. Then she pauses. Yeah, he's here right now, looking for you as a matter of fact, she says, fake smiling at Sonny. We were just having a nice chat, she adds before handing Sonny the phone.

Sonny takes the call in the living room so she can't listen. Harlan wants to hook up for a beer. He doesn't sound pissed but something is definitely wrong. He doesn't even ask what Sonny is doing at Annabelle's.

How'd you know I was here.

Lila said you came by and were headed there next. He says, Just meet me at the Inn, and hangs up.

Sonny hands the phone back to Annabelle, who snatches it from him and slams it back into the cradle. She puts her hands on her hips and cocks one of them to the side. Well, she says.

Well what.

What did that motherfucker want.

Just looking for me, Sonny says. We're gone to get a beer.

He didn't say nothing about me.

Nope, he says. What's there to say.

That no good prick, she says. So you're gone to see him now.

Yeah, I'm gone.

Then let him smell me on you, she thinks, flipping hair out of her face and giving him the puppy dog eyes. He sees it coming from a long mile away. She peels off her shirt over her head and she's not wearing any kind of bra.

Sonny thanks her for the coffee and tries to slide past her to the front door. She follows him and even grabs hold of his collar, and he tries to duck and squirm away.

He really does try.

Harlan is waiting for Sonny out in front of the Conway Inn, having a smoke. What took you he says.

That girl of yours.

What about her.

She's a real pistol is all.

They go inside the bar. Sonny considers telling Harlan what happened back there in Turners but he can't see any good coming from it. Except if he doesn't say shit now Annabelle might try to turn it around on him and make it look bad so Harlan would side with her. In that case it would be better to come clean up front, he figures. But he doesn't think she'll do that. And even though Sonny has never given Harlan any reason to mistrust him, he decides then and there to clam up about the whole thing. He'll tell the whole truth later if it comes down to that.

Did she make a run at you, Harlan says.

Sonny swallows some beer wrong and Harlan slaps him on the back. Jesus, Sonny says. What'd you say.

That's her thing when she's pissed at me, Harlan says. Then she uses it to get at me, you know.

I hope you know I'd never.

I know, Harlan says. But she's got me all twisted.

Sonny fingers the bowl of stale nuts and pretzels.

The rain is coming down so hard that it's also going up. Sonny is drunk now and he watches Harlan fumble with his bike behind the bar. It's no use. He's in no condition to ride anyhow. But there's no talking to Harlan sometimes and Sonny stands there and watches him and eventually Harlan curses and gives up just as a Cadillac edges alongside them. The window comes down a crack and it's Spider inside. He has a couple black girls with him, probably from Holyoke, and a bottle of brown booze in his clutch. He opens the door and Sonny and Harlan get in. It's warm and dry and the stereo is playing some kind of jazzy shit.

My two friends, Spider says. We're looking for you.

The girls giggle. They're all over Spider and it's clear he has agreed to pay them.

So this is how you train for a fight, he says.

Harlan looks at Spider and he looks at each of the girls and he looks at Sonny. Shit, he says.

What you mean.

What I mean is shit, Harlan says.

344

Sonny laughs. The girls giggle. Spider says something to the girls and they laugh at whatever it is. The driver laughs too and then parks across the street. Harlan pushes against the door, gets out of the car.

Let's have a little party together, Spider says.

Sonny follows Harlan into the rain and stands in front of him. Come on, Sonny says. Just a few more drinks.

I don't like it, Harlan says. Don't like that guy.

Come on.

Harlan sways. He's having a hard time keeping his balance and Sonny helps him.

Shit, I haven't seen you this bad in I don't know how long. He steers Harlan to the front door of the Inn and Spider and the girls follow them back inside. They sit at a round table and Sonny lets Harlan fall asleep with his head on it. Spider gets one of the girls to sit with Sonny and rub his leg. Her warm tongue darts in and out of his ear like a hummingbird.

Maybe it's better your friend is drunk, Spider says.

Sonny looks at Harlan.

You and me, we share the pussy tonight, he says.

Sonny raises his glass and there is a funky foursome making its way slowly to the stage. They are old and white-haired but once they started playing rock and roll it doesn't much matter. Spider dances. He twirls his whore around the floor and she throws her head back and laughs like a debutante. Sonny dances with his girl too and when he sits back down Harlan is long fucking gone. Sonny looks at the driver.

Where'd he go, he says.

The driver ignores him and stares straight ahead. Where the fuck is he.

Spider barks at the driver and gets a terse response. Then he turns and faces Sonny and he smiles but not nice.

Your friend, he left, he says. Now it's just us.

Sonny finds Harlan at his father's house. They are both hung and Harlan is lying on the bed and Sonny is on the floor. Lila is making a pot of coffee, says they smell like a whiskey mill.

Is there even a whiskey mill any more, Sonny says.

I guess there is.

Where they actually make the whiskey, Sonny says. At a mill.

That's the official term, Lila says.

Shit, Harlan says. Who the fuck cares.

Well, she said it like she knew what she was talking about.

People say all kind of things with authority.

Sonny looks away. Where'd you end up last night, he says.

Here.

Was the ride all right.

I don't know, Harlan says. I woke up and I was here.

When did you leave.

I don't remember leaving anywhere.

We are at the Inn dancing and then you were gone.

Dancing, Harlan says. I don't dance.

Not you, Sonny says. Me and Spider and them spades.

Harlan doesn't remember any of it. He'd had one of his spells. He doesn't remember seeing Spider. Sonny laughs and Lila comes back with two cups of coffee with milk.

Here you go, boys.

Thanks, Lila.

Yeah, thanks.

She leans against the door frame and watches them. Maybe we can talk later, she says to Harlan.

Sure, Harlan says. What about.

Your father.

What about him.

Let's do it later, she says. If that's okay.

Sonny gets up. I can leave if you want, he says.

No that's okay, Lila says. You boys rest.

Lila goes back up to the house. Sonny sits down.

Harlan closes his eyes and squeezes them. There's no aspirin anywhere. The ghost of the old man starts screaming upstairs and there's some light leaking through the garage and into the room where Lila had left the door open a little bit, dust particles floating in the beam and looking almost religious. Harlan starts to snore

and Sonny removes the mug from his hand so he won't
spill hot coffee on himself. He decides to wait until
Harlan wakes up and then he'll tell him the fight is
scheduled for Tuesday next.

When he hears Annabelle's voice, Harlan thinks he's
dreaming.

What the fuck happened, she says.

There it is again. Harlan opens his eyes. Annabelle
is crying.

Look at you, she says.

He tries to speak but something is wrong with his
mouth. He sits up and looks around. It's Annabelle's
apartment. Everything is all busted up, blood and pieces
of broken glass and furniture everywhere. A kitchen
knife with a busted blade on the floor nearby.

What the fuck did you do, she says.

His memory is coming back. It's not a dream.
Tuesday night, after he beat Spider's guys, both of them,
he came to get Annabelle and that Greek fuck was in her
apartment and they both started yelling and throwing
hands. That's all he can remember before the fog settles
back in.

I think he's dead, Annabelle says. We got to get
out of here.

She helps him stand. His left leg doesn't work
much so he drags it along. Annabelle's Z28 is out front
and she puts him in the back seat and he lies down to rest
because he's so tired. The car starts after two or three

tries and he can smell the gas because she almost flooded it.

Don't pump the gas so much, he says.

What the fuck, she says.

You got the money.

Yeah. Sonny gave it to me.

Good. It's for you.

Jesus. I think he stabbed you in a couple places.

You can go somewhere nice with that much cash.

Oh, baby. Don't talk like that.

Like what.

There's no place nice without you.

He feels along his upper thigh and it seems she's right about him being stabbed. A home-made bandage is in place, an old T-shirt. Some fucking girl, he thinks. But she's driving too fast so he tells her slow down because it doesn't matter now anyhow. None of it does. She's talking, but her voice is slipping away from him. He tries to curl up into a ball in his seat but the pain is finally too much, where he got stuck in the gut too, and so he closes his eyes, and he pictures a simple farmhouse on maybe twenty acres, a horse or two, and a big red barn.

About the Authors

Constantinos Andronis is a self-taught artist. He has exhibited solo in Athens, Eleusis, Crete and participated in numerous group exhibitions in Greece and Italy. His work on Theatre Photography, Venice and Portraiture has been compiled in one monograph (published in 2009), whereas 2017 awaits the publication of a book on Ancient Drama featuring his work. Visit his work at www.c-andronis.gr or contact him at constantinos.alpha@gmail.com

Lane Ashfeldt's writing has been published by theguardian.co.uk, in the pages of anthologies *Punk Fiction, Dancing with Mr Darcy,* and *Down the Angel,* and in literary journals The London Magazine, The Dublin Review, The Journal of Microliterature and Southword. Lane's fiction collection *SaltWater* was published in 2014 by Liberties Press.

Susmita Bhattacharya's debut novel, *The Normal State of Mind,* was published by Parthian in March 2015. Her short stories have appeared in several journals and magazines in the UK and internationally, one of which has been nominated by Structo for the Pushcart Prize. Her short story, 'The Summer of Learning', was recently featured on Radio 4.

Mark Blayney won the Somerset Maugham Prize for *Two Kinds of Silence.* His latest short story collection, *Doppelgangers*, is available from Parthian as is his spoken word collection *Loud music makes you drive faster.* A regular performance poet and MC, Mark's been longlisted for the National Poetry Prize and has been published in Agenda, The London Magazine, The Interpreter's House, Poetry Wales and writes regularly for Wales Arts Review.

Jon Boilard was born and raised in small towns in Western Massachusetts. He has been living in Northern California since 1986. Jon's debut short story collection, *Settright Road* (Dzanc Books/2017), was preceded by two novels, *The Castaway Lounge* (Dzanc Books/2015) and *A River Closely Watched* (MacAdam Cage/2012). *ARCW* was a finalist for the Northern California Book Award. He has participated in the Cork International Short Story Festival in Cork, Ireland, the Wroclaw Short Story Festival in Wroclaw, Poland, and LitQuake in San Francisco, California.

Neil Campbell is from Manchester, England. Twice included in Best British Short Stories (2012 & 2015). Three collections of short fiction, *Broken Doll*, *Pictures from Hopper* and *Ekphrasis*. Two poetry chapbooks, *Birds* and *Bugsworth Diary*. First novel *Sky Hooks* published in September 2016.

Ingrid Casey is a poet, teacher, mother and artist. Her work is informed by art, memory, life in Ireland and the sublime that we find in day to day life. She has developed her craft through having work published in The Moth, Banshee magazine, Southword, the Honest Ulsterman and in the fundraising anthology for the Dublin Simon Community, *Looking at the Stars*.

Nuala O'Connor was born in Dublin, Ireland and lives in East Galway. Her third novel, *Miss Emily*, was shortlisted for The Eason Book Club Novel of the Year 2015 and longlisted for the 2017 International Dublin Literary Award.

Kelly Creighton is the founding editor of The Incubator, and author of *The Bones of It* (Liberties Press) which was selected as the San Diego Review novel of the year 2015 and nominated for the 2016 Kate O'Brien Award. Her short fiction and poems have won Creighton runner-up and short-listings for awards such as the Michael McLaverty Award, Seamus Heaney Award for New Writing, Fish Short Story Prize and Cuirt New Writing Prize. Her short story collection *Bank Holiday Hurricane* will be published in 2017.

Nia Davies is a poet, editor and literary curator based in Wales. Her publications are: *Then spree* (Salt 2012), *Çekoslovakyalılaştıramadıklarımızdanmısınız,* or Long Words (Hafan/Boiled String, 2016) and *All fours* will appear from Bloodaxe in 2017. She is also editor of *Poetry Wales* and has worked on several transcultural literary projects. Her poems have been translated into Arabic, Kurdish, Bangladeshi, Czech, Mandarin, Slovak, Spanish and Turkish.

Born in Derbyshire, **Emily Devane** now lives and writes in Yorkshire. She was a 2016 Word Factory Apprentice. Her stories can be found in The Bath Short Story Award Anthology (2015), Rattletales 4 and 'A Box of Stars Under The Bed' (The National Flash Fiction Day Anthology, 2016). The Nottingham Review recently nominated her story from its Winter edition, 'Back When The Sky Was

Different', for The Best Small Fictions Anthology. She tweets @DevaneEmily.

Mari Ellis Dunning is a Welsh writer of poetry, short stories, children's books and novels. She has work published in various publications, including the New Welsh Review, Female First Magazine, Parthian's Cheval Anthologies, Cultured Vultures and Parthian's *How to Exit a Burning Building*. Mari's ebooks can be found on Amazon or via her blog, while her children's novel, *Percy the Pompom Bear*, is available from Rowanvale Books and other retailers. Mari recently won the Terry Hetherington Young Writers Award, for her short story 'Cartref', and came third place in the Robin Reeves Prize. She was highly commended in the Welsh Poetry Competition.

Jackie Gorman is from Athlone. Her poetry has been published in Wordlegs, The Honest Ulsterman,The Galway Review, Headspace, Bare Hands, Poetry Ireland Review and the UK Journals The Sentinel Literary Quarterly and Obsessed With Pipework. She was highly commended in the Goldsmith International Poetry Competition and the Patrick Kavanagh Poetry Awards in 2015. She received the Phizzfest Poetry

Award in 2016. Her poetry has appeared in the following anthologies: *Ring Around The Moon*, edited by Noel Monahan and *Respond*, edited by Alan McMonagle.

Lander Hawes' novel *Captivity* was published by Unthank Books in 2012. During the last five years Hawes has read stories at Foyles, at 3:AM Magazine, Writers' Centre Norwich and Unthank Books events, at the Short Wonder Short Story Festival, and on BBC Radio Norfolk. His stories have been published in *Being Dad* and *Unthology 2* amongst other places.

Kathy Miles is a poet and short story writer living in West Wales. She has published three collections of poetry: *The Rocking Stone* (Poetry Wales Press), *The Shadow House*, and *Gardening with Deer* (Cinnamon Press). She has also produced an edited anthology of poems and photographs (*The Third Day: Landscape and the Word*) for Gomer Press. Her work has appeared in many anthologies and magazines, and she has been placed in several major competitions, winning the Welsh Poetry Competition in 2014, the Bridport Poetry Prize in 2015, and the PENfro Poetry Competition in 2016.

Kathy frequently reads at local events and festivals, and is a co-editor of The Lampeter Review. She is a founder-member of the Lampeter Writers' Group, formerly run by Gillian Clarke, and a member of Wales PEN Cymru and The Welsh Academy. She has recently completed an MA in Creative Writing at the University of Wales, Trinity Saint David and is currently working on a fourth poetry collection.

Robert Minhinnick is a prize-winning poet, novelist, short story writer and essayist. He has won Wales Book of the Year and the Forward Poetry Prize. He has read at literary festivals around the world.

Derwen Morfayel was born in Spain, bred in Wales and now writes fiction and poetry. She has a degree in Creative Writing and completed her first novel for an MPhil. Her work appears in literary magazines Halcyon, Severine and Shooter as well as on her blog: www.derwenmorfayel.com.

Sue Moules is a poet whose most recent collection is *The Moth Box* (Parthian).

Kate North is the author of *Bistro* (2012), a poetry collection and *Eva Shell* (2008), a novel. She is interested in urban life and the impact of technology on writing and identity. She is also interested in communicating scientific and medical subjects through creative writing. She teaches at Cardiff Metropolitan University.

Bethany W Pope is an award-winning writer. She has published several collections of poetry: *A Radiance* (Cultured Llama, 2012), *Crown of Thorns*, (Oneiros Books, 2013), *The Gospel of Flies* (Writing Knights Press 2014) and *Undisturbed Circles* (Lapwing, 2014). Her fourth full collection, *The Rag and Boneyard* was published by Indigo Dreams in 2016, while her first novel, *Masque,* was published by Seren, also in 2016.

Gary Raymond is a novelist, short story writer, critic, and lecturer in English and Creative Writing. As well as a regular voice in Wales Arts Review, Gary has written for The Guardian, Rolling Stone Magazine, is a theatre critic for The Arts Desk, and is a regular commentator on arts and culture for BBC Wales. He has an MA in Creative Writing from Bath Spa University, and a PGCE in higher education. His debut novel, *For Those Who Come After,* was published by Parthian Books in 2015.

Iain Robinson is an academic and writer living in the East of England. He writes fiction, literary criticism, essays, and reviews. His short fiction has recently appeared in The Missing Slate, Litro, Wales Arts Review and The Lonely Crowd, and has been anthologised in *Being Dad* (Tangent Books) and *Hearing Voices* (Litro). He is a prose editor with Lighthouse Journal.

Jeanette Sheppard is currently working on a collection of flash fiction. Her work has been published in the 2016 and 2014 National Flash Fiction Day anthology and online in Litro Magazine and The Lonely Crowd. She was a winner of Mslexia's monthly Flashcard and has been short-listed for The Fish Flash Fiction Prize and The Short Story's monthly competition. She has also been long-listed for the Bare Fiction Flash Fiction Prize and Flash500.

Nora Shychuk holds an MA in Creative Writing from University College Cork and a BA in Film Screenwriting and English from Jacksonville University.

Tom Vowler's story collection, *The Method*, won the Scott Prize and the Edge Hill Readers' Prize, and his novels include *What Lies Within* and *That Dark Remembered Day*. He is an associate lecturer at Plymouth University, where he completed his PhD. Represented by Ed Victor, Tom is editor of the literary journal *Short FICTION*, and occasional all-rounder for the Authors Cricket XI. His second collection of stories *Dazzling the Gods* is forthcoming in 2017.

About the Editor

John Lavin has a doctorate from the University of Wales, Trinity Saint David, as well as an MA in Creative Writing from Cardiff University. As well as editing The Lonely Crowd, he is also Fiction Editor of Wales Arts Review and edited their short story anthology, *A Fiction Map of Wales*. His short fiction has appeared in The Incubator, Spork Press, Dead Ink, The Lampeter Review and in the recent anthology *Secondary Character*. His criticism has appeared in The Irish Times, Wales Arts Review and The Welsh Agenda amongst other places.